ANIMAL CLOCKS AND COMPASSES

From Animal Migration to Space Travel

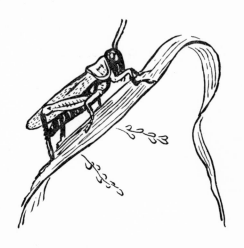

Also by Margaret O. Hyde

ATOMS TODAY AND TOMORROW, New Rev. Ed.

EXPLORING EARTH AND SPACE, New Rev. Ed.

DRIVING TODAY AND TOMORROW

FLIGHT TODAY AND TOMORROW

FROM SUBMARINES TO SATELLITES

MEDICINE IN ACTION

OFF INTO SPACE!

PLANTS TODAY AND TOMORROW

And with Edwin Hyde

WHERE SPEED IS KING

by **MARGARET O. HYDE**

ANIMAL CLOCKS

FROM ANIMAL MIGRATION

illustrated by P. A. Hutchison

WHITTLESEY HOUSE—McGRAW-HILL

AND COMPASSES

TO SPACE TRAVEL

Library of Congress Catalog Card Number: 60-14044

Published by Whittlesey House
A Division of the McGraw-Hill Book Company, Inc.

31592

Acknowledgments

The author wishes to thank the many people who contributed to this book. The following were especially helpful: Professor Frank A. Brown, Northwestern University; Professor Archie Carr, University of Florida; Professor Edward S. Deevey, Yale University; Professor L. C. Dunn, Columbia University; Allen J. Duvall, U.S. Fish and Wildlife Service; Professor Donald R. Griffin, Harvard University; Professor Arthur D. Hasler, University of Wisconsin; Professor Charles Lyman, Harvard University; Dr. G. V. T. Matthews, The Wildfowl Trust, England; Professor Max Renner, University of Munich, Germany; Dr. Franz Sauer, University of Wisconsin.

For Lawrence E. Hyde

Contents

Monarch butterflies

Arctic tern

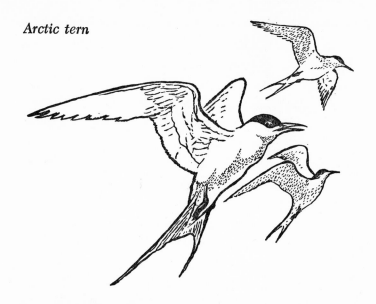

1. *Animal Mysteries*

The world of animals is full of mysteries. Some of these mysteries concern the amazing sense of time and direction which certain animals possess. These animals seem to have internal clocks and compasses.

Have you ever wondered why birds migrate at definite times year after year? How do these birds which travel thousands of miles from one home to another find their way? Even young birds which have never been to a winter home go to the right place. For example, an Arctic tern which is born near the North Pole leaves its home at the age of six weeks and travels about 11,000 miles to the Antarctic. When the days grow shorter in the Southern Hemisphere, it flies back to its nesting place near the North Pole. Think of the navigation problems in traveling from one end of the world to the other and of finding last year's small nesting place at the end of a journey!

Thousands of other kinds of birds make shorter trips when spring and autumn come. They fill the flyways—the routes which they take from one home to another. Other kinds of animals, too, find their way on long journeys. Eels, for example, are fish that leave the streams of Europe and America in the autumn of the year. They travel as much as 5,000 miles to reach the Sargasso Sea which lies far from the shores of the Atlantic Ocean. Monarch butterflies are another example. They rest, from time to time, on their long journeys in such great numbers that they cover every plant in a garden. Then they fly on to the same place which their parents left the year before. How do these animals find their way? What sets the clock for their journeys?

Year after year, at exactly the right time, thousands of animals come out of the sea and deposit their eggs on the warm sand at the edge of the waves where they will not be washed into the sea until the proper time comes. During the winter, Northern fur seals roam the Pacific Ocean. When the right time comes, they reach the island which is their summer home just before they bear their young. From time to time, skies grow black with grasshoppers. Millions sweep across the land and settle on a field like a blanket. They eat the leaves and stalks, leaving the field bare. What triggers such movements? How are they timed?

Even human beings have a sort of internal clock. It has been suggested that the rate at which a person's biological clock "ticks" influences the length of his life. Some scientists believe that all kinds of clocks may run differently on very fast space ships and that someone traveling on such a ship may not age as fast as one does on earth.

While some men are trying to solve the problems of navigation in space, others are searching for the answers to the mysteries of how animals find their way here on earth and of how their clocks run.

Many of the feats which animals perform time after time surpass things of a similar nature that man can do with his superior brain. The wonderful rhythms of animal life, and the strange journeys which some animals make, have puzzled scientists for many years. Today, many men are searching for the answers to these puzzles. Sometimes they solve the puzzles in ways that are just as interesting as the strange habits themselves. Here are some true stories about these animal wonders and the scientists who study them.

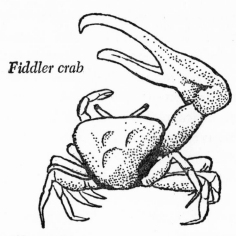

Fiddler crab

2. At the Turn of the Tide

Tides are more important than the clocks on the wall to many people who live along the seacoasts of the world. Twice each day, the waters of the ocean rise, or move higher on the beaches. Twice within the same twenty-four hours, the waters move out. Perhaps you have waited for the tide to come in so that you could fish from the pier, or perhaps you have waited for it to go out so that you could dig clams in the sand. High and low tide times differ slightly each day. Those who live near the sea follow tide time-tables, which are calculated for the tide changes in the months ahead.

The position of the moon and the sun govern the changing tides. At certain times of the month—when the moon and sun pull together or pull in opposite directions—the tides are greatest. Calendars tell us when these times will come. There are many animals who seem to know this time, too, even though they cannot read the calendars. If they did not live in rhythm with the tides, none of their young would survive. And some are affected by the tides in other ways.

FIDDLER CRABS

Can you imagine trying to tell the time of day by looking at the shell of a crab? Strangely enough, it can be done by looking at the shell of a fiddler crab. Fiddler crabs scurry on many sandy and muddy beaches and along salt marshes. They are strange crabs, for a number of reasons. The fathers, or male crabs, have one large front claw which is held much like a violin. This is why they are called fiddler crabs. They use their large claws to fight other male crabs.

All fiddler crabs are strange in other ways. Each morning, about sunrise, fiddler crabs begin to darken. This darkness of their skin helps to protect them from their enemies, for this deeper color is more like that of the beaches on which they run. It also helps to protect their inside organs from the bright sunshine of unshaded beaches. The crabs grow darker, hour by hour, until they are darkest by noon when the sun is shining directly above. By sunset, fiddler crabs are growing paler. They are not a very accurate clock, but if you become familiar with the shades of these crabs by watching them day after day, you might be able to tell the approximate time by the shade of their skin.

Is it sunlight that makes fiddler crabs darken? To find the answer to this question, scientists took crabs from the beach and put them in a completely dark room. The crabs continued to change color day after day, just the way they would have if they were outdoors. No sunshine gave them the signal. Certainly, the fiddler crabs have a sort of built-in clock.

Here is a confusing thing. Light seems to have some effect on the crabs' skin color. Scientists can use light to reset the clocks of fiddler crabs! Imagine some crabs in a completely dark room. From midnight until noon a bright light shines on them; then the crabs are kept in the dark until midnight of the next day. These false days and nights are repeated several times. Day comes six hours earlier than it normally would. The crabs still change color, but the time of the color-change shifts; they are now darkest six hours after midnight, or at six o'clock in the morning, instead of at noon.

Fiddler crabs act as living clocks in another way, too. Each day at low tide fiddler crabs scurry about the beach in search of food. They look hardest at low tide, when the ocean waves cover less of the beach.

If you go to the seashore on your vacation, you know that the low tide does not take place at exactly the same time each day. Today it is fifty minutes later than yesterday. Tomorrow it will be fifty minutes later than it is today. The next day, the low tide will be fifty minutes later. And so it goes, day after day. The fiddler crabs search hardest for food at a time that is fifty minutes later each day. Their mealtime seems to be in rhythm with the tide.

Tides occur at different times in different parts of the world. Imagine two crabs on separate beaches: On Sandy Beach, the low tide takes place at noon today. On Stony Beach, the low tide comes at three in the afternoon. If both crabs are taken from their beaches in the morning, what will happen? Scientists have done this. The crab from Sandy Beach runs hardest at noon, whereas the crab from Stony Beach runs hardest at three in the afternoon. The next day, each will run hardest fifty minutes later. The rhythm of the tides and of color changes seems deeply planted in all fiddler crabs. Day after day, year after year, for millions of years, crabs have run hardest at low tide and have changed color with the passing hours. They will probably continue to do so for millions of years to come, even though no one knows exactly how the crabs "tell time."

HORSESHOE CRABS

Here is a crab that's not really a crab. Horseshoe crabs are animals that live in the sea. They do not belong to the crab family, but are close relatives of spiders. Their shells are shaped somewhat like a

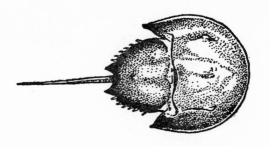

Horseshoe crab

horse's hoof. This is where they get the first part of their name. They look somewhat like huge crabs, too. So most people call these animals horseshoe crabs.

Usually, horseshoe crabs stay in water that is between 12 and 36 feet deep. But once each year, in the spring, when their built-in clocks tell them that it is time to lay eggs, horseshoe crabs come to the shore. They choose the very highest tides of the month. Together they swim to the shallow water and creep to the shore to lay their eggs in the tide-washed shore. Some travel one behind the other, like a little train, while others come to the tide line unattached. Soon after the crabs have made their yearly trip to the shore, you can see thousands of tiny eggs in the little troughs which are the ripple marks of the sand. Many of the eggs are eaten by hungry fish who find them almost as soon as they are laid. Sandpipers make a meal of thousands of others. But some will grow into young horseshoe crabs.

A month after the eggs have been laid, the waters

of another high tide wash away the sand and break open the egg shells. Tiny creatures come out of the shells and are washed into the shallow waters. Now the young animals do not look much like their parents. But in time they will cast off their new shells, grow tails, and look just like small horseshoe crabs. They will cast off shells as they grow, again and again. Each horseshoe crab that manages to live to grow up in the sea will stay within a few miles of the place of his birth and come home to lay eggs at the turn of the tide.

Why does the horseshoe crab come to the shore at a certain time? Recently, scientists have learned that a horseshoe crab can see rays of light known as ultraviolet and infrared. People cannot see these. Perhaps a horseshoe crab can, in some strange way use these lights to find his way to the place of his birth. But these do not set his built-in clock.

This trip to shore is a migration which has taken place for millions of years. Each year, in the spring and early summer, you can be sure that horseshoe crabs will come to the edge of the sea for thousands of miles along the Atlantic Coast.

GRUNION ON THE BEACH

Have you ever heard of a grunion? If you go to the coast of southern California at exactly the right time of the year, you can have fun gathering grunion at night from the beach. Imagine yourself standing

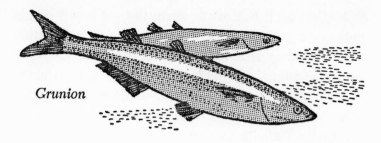

Grunion

on the gleaming beach on a May evening when the highest tide of the season is rolling in. The moon is just past full, and the sky is clear. Slim silver bodies of small fish glisten on the crest of each wave that beats upon the shore. These are grunion. They let themselves be carried nearly to the beach, then they flick their tails and turn back. They are waiting for the very wave that rolls farthest up the beach. That is the time of the turn of the tide.

Grunion choose the highest wave as accurately as the most complicated machine that can be used to find out when it will come. The moon, thousands of miles away, and the sun, millions of miles away, determine when this time will come. The grunion are so accurate that man can figure out the time of the tide for any past or future day by using information he gets by watching them.

Suddenly a wave breaks just a few inches shorter than the one before it—the tide has turned. The grunion let themselves be rolled onto the sand, and before the next wave comes, the females lay the eggs and the males deposit a material known as "milt."

This fertilizes the eggs and makes it possible for them to grow into young fish. The wave which follows the one that carried the parents to the sand, carries them back to the sea.

You must run fast to gather the grunion. There are thousands of them flopping on the wet sand making the whole beach appear shimmering silver. The time is short, but the grunion are many.

When the grunion have gone, the eggs are still buried in the sand. Here they stay for two weeks while the warm sun shines on the sand. Then, when the moon is new, the tide is at its height again. Waves come higher and higher on the beach until they reach the eggs buried in the sand. A wave frees the eggs. Within a few minutes baby grunion hatch and are washed out to sea. When they grow up they, too, will time their egg laying with the same exactness as their parents did.

Suppose grunion did not have this sense of timing. If they deposited eggs when the tide continued to rise, the waves that reached higher and higher on the beach would carry the eggs off to sea before the young had a chance to begin their growth in the sun-warmed sand. That would be the end of the grunion.

How do grunion choose the right time to lay their eggs on the beach? The exact time of high tide differs by fifty minutes each day. And some days the high tide is higher than on others. This happens on the nights when the moon is full and when the moon is new. It is on such a night, when the tide has just turned, that the grunion "run." On such a night, the people who make a sport of catching them come to the beaches.

Grunion live in just one part of the world. They come only to the beaches of southern California. But there are many other kinds of animals around the world that can sense the turn of the tide. For instance, some kinds of shrimp come out of the sea at certain times. But no matter what kind of an animal it is, the mystery remains the same. How do they time their movements? How do they navigate?

SEA WORMS

Scientists have studied a little sea worm which depends on the light of the sun to help with its food problem. It eats a certain kind of green seaweed. When the tide goes out, this sea worm suns himself. While it is taking this sun bath, the seaweed is absorbing the sunlight and makes starch and sugar which is used as food by the little animal. Before the tide comes in, the little sea worm burrows in the sand so that it will not be carried out to sea. The waves roll over it, but it is safely tucked in the sand beneath them.

Suppose an indoor home is made for some of these worms in a tank filled with sand that is moistened with salt water. In such a home these worms come to the surface of the sand twice a day for their sun baths even though they are indoors. Twice a day they burrow in the sand, just as if they were on the beach where the waves might wash them away. Their built-in clocks are still set to the rhythm of the tides.

REEF HERONS

Herons are long-legged wading birds with sharp, slender beaks. They are found throughout the world. On the mainland of Australia, there is a kind of heron that is an expert at knowing the turn of the tides. It may live as far as 30 miles from the shore, but each day the reef heron departs from its roost to make a trip to the reefs for food. It leaves at exactly the proper time so that it reaches the edge of the sea at low tide. Then it can feed on the animals which are exposed. Because of the difference in the time of low tide, its clock must be set fifty minutes later each day.

There are many animals whose lives are adjusted to the rhythms of the tides. They need no clock on the wall, no calendar of tides, to tell them when the waters will reach the highest point on the beach or ebb away from the shore.

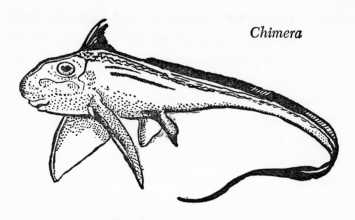

Chimera

3. Journeys to the Sea

The paths of animals crisscross oceans like a great network of highways. At all times, there are sea creatures whose impulses are driving them to migrate to another part of the sea. In addition to those animals who come to the edge of the sea at the turn of the tide, there are fish that migrate from cold water to warm; there are many also who move from the deep waters where they spend the winter to the more shallow waters where they breed in the spring. Sharks, rays, or skates, flatfish such as flounders, and many other kinds follow this pattern. The rabbit fish, or Arctic chimera, is believed to spend the winter at a depth of about 500 fathoms in the North Atlantic, the Mediterranean, and the South Atlantic Ocean. In the spring and early summer, some travel to the coast of the United States; others go to the waters of Norway, Scotland, or Ireland for spawning.

Shrimp and some other animals travel back and forth from deep to shallow water but, unlike most creatures of the sea, they bear their young in the deep. To make certain of their movements, shrimp are marked with small celluloid tags. Colored dyes are injected into other fish to mark them. Careful records are then kept of where the fish were found. After the information is recorded, the shrimp are put back into the sea and allowed to travel where they will. From the records of thousands of such shrimp, fishermen have learned where and when to cast their nets.

Some animals travel much farther than others. Some even come out of the ocean and travel far up the rivers to spawn. Others travel from the rivers to the ocean. And there are migrations of land animals which end in the sea. These strange journeys happen again and again. They are not just accidents, but journeys that are controlled by nature's clocks and compasses.

The journeys of the salmon belong to this group.

WONDERS OF THE SALMON

Have you ever eaten salmon for dinner? Many millions of these fish are caught each year. Some are eaten fresh, but most are canned. Those that escape the fishermen and are not eaten by other fish, may live to complete one of the most amazing journeys in the

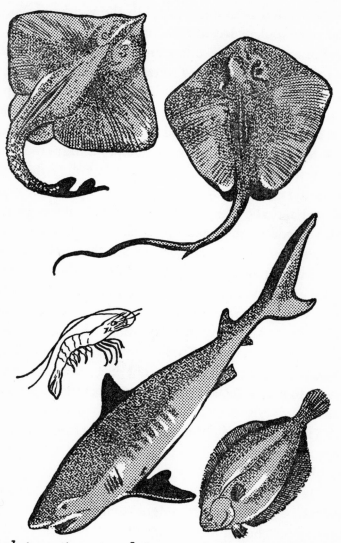

A skate, a sting ray, a shrimp, a tiger shark, and a flounder

world. In some strange way the salmon know when the right time comes for them to lay their eggs in the shallow waters of the same streams in which they were born, and they find their way to these streams from great distances.

Imagine a Pacific salmon, heavy with eggs. She is swimming over the small pebbles that lie on the bottom of the stream in the shallow water. She swishes away the mud and small plants with her tail and body to make a nest that is about as wide as a person is tall. She scrapes her belly over the stones and deposits 30,000 eggs, each a heavy pink globule about the size of a pea. The eggs fall to the bottom. At once, a male fish swims over the eggs and deposits his milt to fertilize them. Without this, the eggs would not hatch.

Life begins to stir inside the eggs. For many of them, life is short, for thousands are eaten by fish before they have a chance to grow. But some of the many thousands of eggs survive, and young fish take shape in the eggs from which they hatch. When they are about an inch long, the tiny fish lie motionless on the bottom of the stream, feeding on the yolk sac that hangs from their bellies. After about two and a half months, this food has been used. Then the young fish must search for food themselves. They shoot through the water after insects, but many of the fish become food for larger fish.

By the second winter, these Pacific salmon that are still alive gather together. They swim in a group so

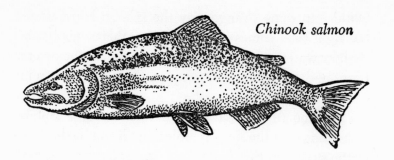

Chinook salmon

that each movement seems to be felt by all. They move as waves through the water. Then spring rains and melting snow fill the brook. The salmon face the current while they let themselves be carried backward by it toward the sea. Some of the fish are marked by scientists in an effort to learn more about the lives of salmon. Follow a fish marked 404 through the water. During the day he swims against the current and hunts for food. When night comes, Salmon 404 and other salmon ride backward with the current in the middle of the stream.

Now the stream flows into a larger one and the salmon go with it. Bear, mink, racoons and ducks catch many of the fish, but 404 escapes. Weeks pass, and the journey continues for the fish that are not caught. The place of their birth is far behind. Next comes the river. Months pass before the salmon are carried to the sea.

The salt water mingles with the fresh water, and the salmon enter an entirely different world. Over the sandbars, they eat their first ocean food. There are small shrimp and other sea creatures which drift among the plants of the sea. Salmon 404 drifts north with the food. He grows larger as he feeds on herring and other small fish.

Just as the salmon eat smaller fish, the larger fish eat the salmon. Sharks swallow many of them. Diving ducks and loons snatch them from the water. Sea bass and cod take their toll. But Salmon 404 can shoot like an arrow through the water. He is faster than the rest and he escapes.

Day after day, Salmon 404 swims through the ocean waters. You would think him a beautiful sight if you could see his silver-blue back and red-spotted pink belly streaking through the water. He travels for hundreds of miles and he reaches a weight of 20 pounds.

Then the day comes when Salmon 404 begins the long journey home. Something makes him set his course for the shore. In a wonderful but mysterious way, Salmon 404 finds the mouth of the very river from which he came. He sometimes travels as much as 60 miles a day. Other fish who have come from this river join him in his journey. On he goes, from the salt water to fresh water. He has a very strong urge to reach the place where he was born. The way is not easy and the distance is far. He is hundreds of miles from the places where he hunted in the sea. He has hundreds of miles to travel before he reaches the end of his journey. But he travels on.

Fishermen with baited hooks dangle them in the water. The returning salmon are in fine condition. They would make a good catch. Most of the salmon refuse to eat. Their bodies are heavy with layers of fat that will provide enough energy for the hard trip ahead. But some snap at the bait because they think they are attacking an enemy. Other fishermen lay long nets and catch salmon by the thousands. But 404 gets safely by.

Now there is another difficult part of the journey. A dam has been built across the stream. Salmon 404 must find his way up the fish ladder which has been built to help returning salmon. He jumps from step to step and swims across the level top. Each little pool is slightly higher than the one behind it. And so he passes the top of the ladder to continue the journey. Now his food supply is getting low and his beautiful color has disappeared. After traveling upstream for weeks at a time, he rests, but never eats. Again, he has the urge to continue.

After months of traveling, Salmon 404 has reached his birthplace in the shallow part of the stream. Here, in the icy waters, he finds a female preparing a nest after her long journey upstream. Just after her eggs are laid, he deposits the milt. Then he lets the current carry him away. He floats head downward in the stream. In a few days he dies and becomes a meal for a hungry bear that fishes him out of the river.

The salmon marked 404 has made his journey to the

sea and come back to the place of his birth. His young will do the same. When the right time comes, salmon journey to the sea. And when the right time comes, they return to produce their young and, in the case of Pacific salmon, die.

Not all salmon die after spawning. The Atlantic salmon follow a different life pattern. They return to the ocean from their home streams. They come from the Atlantic coast of North America from New England northward, and from the Atlantic coast of Europe from Spain northward. Spawning takes place in the fall, but the adult fish do not go back to the sea until spring. Then they may return in a year, or they may let several years go by before making the hard trip up the river to spawn.

Many scientists have tried to explain how salmon find their way to the place where they began life. No one knows exactly why the fish behave the way they do, but it is certain that many can find their way. For instance, fish that hatch in the laboratory pools of the University of Washington are tagged each year. They travel to the high seas, and fight their way up a fish ladder to return to their homes. Many are killed before they reach the ponds. Thousands begin the journey, but just a few hundred complete it. Think how wonderful it is that any fish get back at all. The tags prove that the fish which return are the same ones which were born in the laboratory pools.

As of today, no one knows the entire story. At one

time it was believed that the salmon went back to the rivers for more oxygen, since there is more oxygen in rivers than in oceans. This seemed like a good reason until it was found that there is less oxygen where the rivers meet the sea than in either the rivers themselves or in the oceans. It does not seem reasonable to believe that salmon know what is beyond the river mouths. So this idea is no longer in favor.

Perhaps the salmon use the sun to find their way to the mouths of the rivers from which they came. Many kinds of fish are known to have the ability to tell direction from the position of the sun. They use their built-in clocks to take the time of day into account when determining their direction in this manner.

When they reach the mouth of the river, salmon are believed to use another kind of a compass. Some scientists believe that salmon can "remember" the characteristics of their home streams throughout their long stays in the ocean. Water samples have been taken from various streams and tested for certain characteristics. Such tests showed that they remained the same throughout the different season of the year, but each differed from the others because of the organic substances dissolved in it. Perhaps there is a different taste to each stream which helps the salmon identify its home. Certainly it is true that adult fish have shown a very sensitive taste ability when they were tested.

No matter what the reason, it is certain that many

salmon use some sort of clock and compass to return from the sea to their place of birth. It may be that these fish use a sense of smell to recognize the materials dissolved in the river which they left in their early days. To test this idea, salmon nostrils have been plugged. When this was done, the fish could not find their own streams. Perhaps this is part of the answer to the built-in compasses; but there is still much to learn.

CRADLE FOR EELS

Here is a strange animal that seems to use a built-in clock and compass for journeys that are the opposite of the salmon's. This long, snake-like animal lurks in the mud of large puddles. It is an eel—a kind of fish that looks like a snake. At night it crawls out of the mud and prowls around for food. An eel finds frogs and toads to eat in the meadow and almost any kind of animal or plant; it does not matter if the food is living or dead.

Most fish cannot stay out of the water for very long, but eels have a special kind of breathing arrangement so they can wriggle across the land and can search for food on land as well as in the water.

How would you like to have an eel for dinner? Many people make food of the eels and find them very tasty. However, many people also refuse to eat eels because they look so much like snakes, and they do not like the idea of eating snakes.

Eels are more famous for their strange habits than they are as a food. For many years no one knew where baby eels were born. At one time, people claimed that they grew out of the dew that fell on banks of ponds and rivers. The Greeks thought they came from earth-

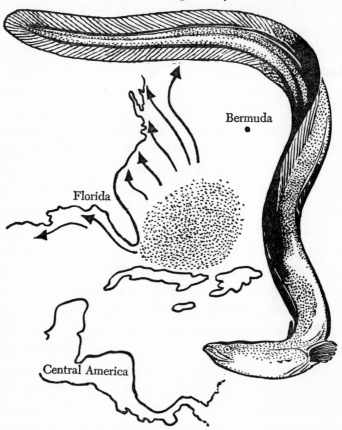

Eels breed in the Sargasso Sea, which is shown here in dotted area. Arrows indicate the path taken by larvae of American eels.

worms. Others thought that eels were produced in various magical ways. One such idea was that horse hairs came to life in rain barrels and developed into eels. The true story of the fresh-water eel is perhaps as amazing as anything that people ever imagined.

The story begins far out in the Atlantic Ocean, where a salty jungle of seaweeds grows under sunny skies. Here lies the Sargasso Sea, where the winds and waves are quiet and currents of the ocean flow around the edges. About ten million tons of plants float in these warm waters and millions of animals live among them. It is here that the sailors of Columbus' day feared that they might be trapped among the seaweeds. This probably never really happened, for the Sargasso Sea is almost as large as the United States and the seaweed is spread out over this great distance. Certainly, the ghost ships that such sailors claimed to see drifting in the clinging weeds were just imagined.

Strange things however, do happen among the floating weeds. Here is the eel's cradle. Can you believe that one fish lays as many as 8 million eggs? This many have been found in a single female eel. Imagine this snake-like fish laying these millions of eggs hundreds of feet below the surface of the water. The bottom of the ocean is several miles below, but the eggs do not fall to the bottom. Each one contains a tiny drop of oil which keeps it from falling through the colder waters below. The eggs are fertilized by a male eel and hang among the seaweed for several weeks. When the young are hatched, they too have a drop of oil in their food sac to keep them from sinking. Soon they begin to rise slowly to the surface. Millions of the young animals spread out in all directions. Each one is clear as glass so that you could read the print on this page right through it, and each one is flat and shaped more like a leaf than like a full-grown eel. These tiny creatures are less than an inch in length, but somehow each manages to choose the proper current at the edge of the Sargasso Sea. The current will carry the eel toward the fresh water of a river. American eels choose a westward current, European eels choose an eastward one. How does each one know where to go? It is not just chance, for the eels are of a different variety. The European eels have fewer bones in their backs than the American eels. No one knows what they use as their compasses, but year after year the eels find their way.

Eels drift along on the proper currents for a long time. American eels reach fresh water rivers when they are a year old. It takes young eels almost three years to reach the shores of Europe or Africa. While they drift, their organs develop and they grow larger and fatter. When they reach the shore, their physical appearance begins to change. Their tiny teeth fall out and they stop eating until they grow a new set. Each young eel is about 2 inches long and as thin as the lead in a pencil. Many elvers, as the young eels are called, swim closely together so that they look somewhat like a rope struggling upstream. They actually attach themselves to each other and push forward against the current. Alone, a young eel might be carried back to the sea, but the rope makes headway. Upstream, the eels separate and settle in pools where they hunt shrimp-like creatures for their food. When fields are wet with dew, some eels manage to slither across them and find their way to ponds far from the streams. Sometimes eels live for years at the bottom of wells that are as far as half a mile from the stream to which they traveled from the sea. In the streams, ponds, and wells, eels grow large and fat. Some reach a length of 5 feet. But when they are from seven to fifteen years old, a curious impulse sends all those that can reach the stream back to the sea.

Not all eels journey up the streams. The ones which do will become the females. Other eels, those which will become males, stay at the bottom of the rivers feeding in the brackish water until they join the females who are returning to the sea. When this time comes, the eels head for their seaweed home without stopping to rest or eat until they have reached it. Their built-in compasses lead them back to the place of their birth. Here they reproduce and die, for this is the end of their strange journey to the sea.

35

4. Road Maps in the Sky

BIRD TRAVELERS

In the fall of this year, about 15 billion birds will fly south from their homes in North America to their winter quarters. Next spring, not so many will fly north again, for migration takes a terrible toll. Some birds are lost in fogs, some are confused by bright lights and crash into the high buildings from which they shine. Tall bridges, piers, monuments, lightships and other aerial obstructions are responsible for great destruction of migrating birds. Local storms and hunters take their toll. Perhaps only half of the birds who journeyed south in the fall will return in the spring. But billions of birds travel great distances and safely return to the same areas which they left the year before.

Over the United States there are four main north-and-south routes known as flyways. They follow the coasts, rivers, and mountains. Other birds fly over oceans, while the birds of Europe and Asia take definite routes to the land which lies south of them.

The greatest of all bird travelers is the Arctic tern which flies about 22,000 miles each year. These gray and white birds whose red beaks are sharp and pointed have been called the migration champions of the world. Because of the earth's tilt at the Antarctic, many of these terns live in uninterrupted daylight—until the sun starts to sink below the horizon for a short period each night. When this occurs, they fly to Europe, cross to North America, and make their nests somewhere between Massachusetts and the North Pole. Many of the birds fly far enough north to live in continuous daylight at this part of the earth for now the earth is in such a position that there is constant daylight at the North Pole. All this daylight gives them plenty of time for food-hunting at the far ends of the earth.

Golden plovers are famous travelers, too. They are not much larger than robins, but Atlantic golden plovers follow a water route from Nova Scotia to their winter homes for more than 2,000 miles non-stop. Some golden plovers stop for food at islands such as Bermuda and the West Indies, but others continue their journeys to their winter quarters in Brazil without stopping. These birds cannot rest on the surface of the water the way a duck can, but must fly from one piece of land to another. Pacific golden plovers fly

The Arctic tern is the greatest of bird travelers.

non-stop for about 2,000 miles from the Aleutian Islands of Alaska to Hawaii on their way to more southern islands where they spend the winter months.

The beautiful little hummingbirds which you may see in a garden in the eastern part of the United States are great travelers, too. These tiny birds fly south for the winter, crossing 500 miles of water over the Gulf of Mexico when they make their way to their winter homes in Central America.

Whooping cranes are famous because there are so few of them left in the world. Each April they leave their home in Texas for their breeding grounds in Canada that are 2,500 miles away. Six months later, scientists watch for them to come back with the young birds. This is an exciting watch, for each bird who meets with disaster on the long flight lowers the already small count of the world population. In 1960, there were only 39 birds, but even this was greater than any count since scientists started keeping score about twenty years before. In the case of whooping cranes, if one bird gets off the path during migration, it is missed. Such was the case when a whooping crane flew the wrong way and landed in Missouri. But most other birds that die en route or lose their way are seldom noticed, because the list of those that find the way is long.

Just a few of the many kinds of bird travelers who fly from one home to another, year after year, have been mentioned here.

Golden plover, left, and whooping crane

KINDS OF MIGRATION

Birds travel in many different patterns. Some never move very far from where they are hatched. They move about locally, leaving their nesting areas in the winter in search for food. There are birds who leave the snowy mountaintops to winter in the valleys below. Such a migration is called a vertical one. Other birds have short distances between summer and winter homes. Robins appear all the year round in some places, for the ranges of different birds overlap. Those that live there in the summer move farther south for the winter, while those that live there in the winter have come from homes that are farther north. No one bird travels far, but each one migrates. Other birds travel greater and greater distances, but none go farther than the Arctic terns.

Many sea birds feed over a whole ocean but breed only in certain nesting spots. Sometimes these travel thousands of miles from their nests, but their built-in clocks and compasses enable them to find their homes when the proper time comes.

Albatross

BIRD COMPASSES

This ability to find a nesting site was well demonstrated by albatrosses. These birds are found over most of the oceans of the world, with the exception of the North Atlantic. Hundreds of thousands of them use Midway Island in the Pacific Ocean as a nesting place. Even though the birds spend most of their lives flying above the oceans, they come home to nest at the age of five. Enough albatrosses, or gooney birds, as they are called, take off from Midway Island to be a hazard to the United States Navy planes which use the island, too. The albatrosses find the airport runways fine for their own take-offs and landings. Sometimes planes and birds collide with often damaging results for both. In an effort to get rid of the albatrosses, Navy men marked some of the birds with pink dye and flew them to far-off places as an experiment. If these stayed away from the island, others were to follow. Before two months were over, birds returned from Japan, the Philippines, Alaska, and the state of Washington in the United States. Some flew as far as 5,000 miles and found their home on the small island of Midway.

By marking birds with bands, much has been learned about their ability to navigate and about the routes that they take. Bird banders are at work all over the world. In North America alone there are over 2,000 people who catch about 500,000 birds each year, fasten aluminum bands around their legs, and release them. About 11 million birds are flying around with bands on their legs. Banding does not hurt a bird. In fact, many come back to the traps for food so many times that they are a nuisance to bird banders.

There are many ways of trapping birds. Nets are used at some banding stations instead of metal traps. Birds are leg-banded while enmeshed in the net and then set free. Each bird is given a number, and information about the bird is recorded so it can be compared with information sent in by the person who finds it next. Perhaps you will someday find a bird which is banded with a metal strip on which there is a number and a request that says, "Notify Fish and Wildlife Service, Washington, D.C."

Some of the first birds to be banded were penguins in Antarctica. Green celluloid bands tied to their legs showed that they came back to the exact same breeding area the following spring. Adélie penguins spend the winter at sea hunting for food. In the early spring, these penguins begin their long walk over frozen seas to the breeding grounds on the coast of the land.

42

Some walk as much as 60 miles to reach the rookery. A penguin cannot see much more than a few yards in

Emperor penguin, left, and Adélie penguin

front of itself, but it manages to go straight to the spot where it nested the year before. Even if the nest area is covered with a foot of snow, a penguin can find it.

Another variety of penguin, the emperor penguin, breeds in Antarctica, too, but these birds travel south toward the pole to have their young in the winter in icy Antarctica where temperatures range below –40 degrees Fahrenheit. A mother emperor penguin balances an egg on her warm feet as she huddles together with many other mothers in the Antarctic night. When spring arrives, the young chicks are ready to migrate north with their parents. At this time, the Adélies are coming south for the summer to breed.

One famous journey to a nest is that of a bird known as the Manx shearwater. These sea-gull-like birds have long slender wings and usually fly close to the waves. They land in order to lay their eggs in holes which they dig in the ground or under rocks. One of these birds was sent by Dr. G. V. T. Matthews of Cambridge University in Britain, by plane to Boston, Massachusetts, where it was released. It flew home in twelve and a half days, where it found its own burrow. A letter telling Dr. Matthews of the bird's release reached him half a day later than the bird. How did this bird find its way over the trackless ocean which lay below most of its 3,000-mile journey?

Another variety of shearwater is among the many birds which arrive at their nesting places on a definite time schedule. The slender-bill shearwaters fly about the North Pacific visiting as far north as Alaska. They nest in tremendous numbers on islands near Australia. When a few arrive in November, more can be expected the very next day, and thousands on the day after that. Almost all reach their destination on that third day, year after year. It is amazing enough that these birds can find their nesting sites, and even more

Shearwater

amazing that they reach them with such precise timing.

Do young birds find their way with help from the older, experienced ones? Sometimes the older birds seem to lead the way, but this is not always the case. To prove that young are born knowing the way, several experiments were performed. Storks from eastern Germany migrate to the Nile Valley, following a route which takes them over Greece and Asia Minor, while the storks of western Germany travel over France and Spain and the northern coast of Africa to Egypt. Scientists traded eggs in the nests of these birds. When they hatched, the young followed the routes of their real parents, not those of the birds who hatched them and lived with them.

Professor William Rowan kept young crows away from their parents who migrated from Edmonton, Alberta in Canada, to central Oklahoma. The young crows, who were marked, were recovered in the wintering area in Oklahoma even though they were not released until a month after the older crows had left for the south.

Another illustration which shows that birds are born knowing where and how far to fly exists in the case of certain cuckoos and American cowbirds, who place their eggs in the nests of other kinds of birds. When the young birds hatch, they go to the winter homes of their own parents instead of migrating with the birds who hatched them.

Stork, left, and homing pigeon

There seems to be no question that the ability to find a winter or summer home is inborn in migrating birds; but there are many questions as to how they steer and know how far to go. Many attempts have been made to explain the mystery of how birds migrate. Birds are known to possess a wonderful sense of vision. Those who fly by day may take advantage of landmarks such as mountains, lakes, coastlines, and rivers. Homing pigeons seem to see landmarks, and day migrators may make some use of them. But landmarks do not guide the birds who have never made the flight before.

Dr. G. V. T. Matthews of Cambridge University, the same scientist who experimented with the shearwater, experimented with pigeons and their use of landmarks. He transported pigeons in cages that were completely lightproof, and he turned the cages many times during the journey from home so that the birds could not tell how many turns were made on the way. These pigeons homed just as well as those which could watch the landscape on the trip. There

Crow, left, cowbird, center, and cuckoo

must be more to finding the way than following landmarks.

Magnetism has been popular as a means of explaining how birds could find their way. Some people believed that birds could detect the direction of the earth's magnetic poles by some sort of built-in compass. To show whether or not this was true, scientists experimented many times with pigeons. They tied strong magnets to some of the pigeons in a group so that the magnets would produce a magnetic field much stronger than the earth's. If pigeons used the natural magnetic field as a compass, this would confuse them so that they would not be able to reach home. But the pigeons who carried magnets reached home just as well as those in the group who had none.

Many people have suggested that birds are guided by a sense of direction centered in the ears which enables them to identify air currents. Others have suggested that the curious forces set up by the rotating earth guide them. Still others believe radio waves are responsible for the ability of birds to find their way. Experiments trying to prove these ideas have resulted in confusing evidence; but recently, some experiments have helped to solve the riddle.

Dr. Gustav Kramer of Germany, proved that migrating birds make use of the sun as a guide. He put some starlings in a specially-built cage through which they could see only the sky above them. He had already noticed that caged birds became restless as the time came when they would migrate if they were free to do so. In this specially-built cage, Dr. Kramer watched the positions of the birds and found that they assumed the position they would take if free to fly to their winter homes. When Dr. Kramer covered the windows so that the sky could not be seen, the birds no longer took this position.

What would happen if an artificial sun were made to travel above the birds? Dr. Kramer found out by using an artificial sun in a position different from the natural one. His birds directed themselves according to the false sun, using it for a guide in finding the direction of migration.

COMPASSES AND CLOCKS COMBINED

Dr. G. T. V. Matthews in England discovered independently that wild birds can use the sun as a compass in such a way that they take its changing position into account. For this, they need a built-in clock which can adjust to the time of the year as well as the time of the day. On any day when the sun is not covered by clouds, birds can estimate the sun's position in the sky compared with what it would be at noon. They use their built-in sextants to estimate the difference between the sun's position at noon where they are flying with the sun's noon position at home. Then they fly in a direction which will give them a better match to the position of the sun at home.

Pigeons and shearwaters have been put to numerous tests to see if they could find their way when unable to see the sun. Dr. Matthews released twenty-five birds at the start of ten days of cloudy weather. The birds were so confused that five never reached home. Others were late, perhaps because they could not see the position of the sun in the sky.

To some people, it seems impossible to believe that birds can keep their internal clocks set on home position, but perhaps this is no more wonderful than the ability of birds to keep their internal temperatures the same no matter what the weather outdoors.

A bird's clock seems to be regulated by the rhythm of day and night. The birds' time-keeping ability is well demonstrated by their pre-dawn singing. When pigeons were kept in cages with artificial day and night, their homing ability was confused. Those whose clocks were set by an artificial dawn that was ahead of schedule imagined themselves west of their homes and flew eastward, just as one would expect them to fly.

The sun theory of bird navigation is one which helps to explain how birds can find their way by day, but many small birds migrate at night. A steady night-long passage of migratory birds has been recorded. As many as 9,000 birds have been observed in one hour by scientists using a telescope on the night of a full moon. How do these birds find their way?

The maps in the sky which are used by warblers in Germany and southwest Africa have been demonstrated by Dr. E. G. F. Sauer at the University of Freiburg. Warblers raise their young during the summer in Europe. In the late summer and early fall, warblers fly at night southward to various parts of Africa. Each small bird, weighing only about three-quarters of an ounce, flies alone at night from its summer home to its winter one without losing its way. Sometimes it covers 100 miles in a single night. In the spring the warblers fly north to raise their young. The young, too, will fly alone the following fall across the same route without being taught where to go or how to get there.

There are more than a hundred types of warblers.

No one knows how they know where to go, but Dr. Sauer's experiments have thrown new light on what they use as a guide. In early experiments, warblers were raised in closed, soundproof chambers where they had no clue as to what the season was outside. They lived in artificial summer all through the year. But when the autumn came outdoors, the birds grew restless and fluttered from branch to branch night after night. This continued for the length of time it would have taken them to fly to Africa. Then they slept at night just as they would in their winter homes. When spring came, the birds were restless at night once more. Their built-in clocks told them it was time to migrate to their European homes, for no clue was given to them in the closed chambers.

Certainly, the birds were ready to migrate when the proper time came, but this did not explain how they found the way. To explore this question, Dr. Sauer placed warblers in a cage with a glass opening at the top. This enabled them to see a portion of the night sky but nothing else around them. When migration time came, the birds faced the direction which they would have traveled at night if they had been free. Even when their perch was turned around, they turned back to the direction they would take. In the spring these directions were opposite of what they were in the fall. Even the young ones who had never experienced a journey to Africa and back, turned the correct way.

The only clue which gave the birds their direction was the starry sky which they could see through the glass top of the cage. Tests showed that when they could not see the stars they became confused. Even meteors streaking through the sky made them change their direction for a moment.

Dr. Sauer and his wife who worked with him carried their experiments even further. They placed the birds in a planetarium which showed a replica of the natural sky. The birds took up their proper direction when the planetarium stars matched the real ones, but when nothing but diffused light was present, they were confused. The stars in the planetarium were shifted so that they appeared to the birds as they would look in different parts of the world. At some times the stars appeared as they would farther south, or farther east. Experiments showed that warblers knew the right direction for all these places at their very first glimpse at the sky. They have built-in time clocks which adjust their course as the night goes on. They can locate themselves by the constellations and so find the way to their summer home and their winter home.

Dr. Sauer is experimenting by removing constellations from his planetarium sky one at a time in an effort to find out what specific pattern of stars is used by the birds.

When they fly in the day, warblers can guide themselves by the position of the sun. On cloudy nights they may use landmarks such as mountain ranges and coastlines. But thick clouds, heavy rains, and fogs confuse them. Their migration stops until their navigational guides can be seen again.

WHAT SETS THE CLOCK?

There is still much mystery about the capacity of birds to follow the same route year after year across continents and oceans; but the knowledge that birds can use the sun and stars as maps helps to solve part of the riddle. No one knows how their flight routes are fixed. How can the ability to find their way be inherited?

Certainly, migrations of birds have been taking place for many years. No one knows exactly how this habit originated. Two of the theories give opposite reasons. One claims that in earlier ages birds lived all over the Northern Hemisphere, with suitable conditions for eating and breeding the year round. When the glacial ice fields advanced, birds were forced southward until all lived in southern areas. As the ice cap retreated, the birds whose ancestral homes were in the north returned to them each spring. They would be driven south again by the advancing ice which came with winter. This happened year after year until it became a fixed habit. This theory is known as the northern ancestral home theory.

The southern ancestral home theory supposes that all birds once lived in the tropics. When they became overcrowded, birds sought breeding grounds where competition was not so great. Those who went north in the summer were forced to return in the winter, but as the ice retreated they flew north again. Thus the birds habitually returned to the north for breeding and to their winter homes soon after the nesting season.

In either case, whether the original home was in the north or south, favorable conditions for breeding in summer and good places for feeding in winter seem to be involved with the origin of migration.

Some scientists believe that change in the length of day stimulates migration anew each year. They believe that the amount of light is more important in triggering migration than the need for more food, since many birds begin their flight before the food supply becomes scarce. The light stimulus may be tied in with the regularity of departure, for light maintains a regularity, too. Temperature varies from day to day, and even from year to year, but the duration of light on any given day is the same each year and has been the same for millions of years in the past.

When days grow longer, birds have more time in which to feed. Their weight increases and the organs of reproduction grow ready to perform their functions. Poultry farmers know that increased light in winter in the henhouse stimulates egg-laying, and they make use of this fact by using artificial lights to make winter days as long as summer ones. Perhaps the changing day length summons the birds from the south and the ocean birds from their flights far from home to their nesting sites.

Experiments with increased light resulted in the growth of reproductive organs in birds that were kept outdoors in temperatures as low as —44 degrees Fahrenheit. When light duration was reduced, the organs returned to their normal condition for the winter.

Some scientists believed that the increased amount of exercise taken on the longer days is responsible for the sexual development. They forced certain birds to exercise in cages where the light was kept very low. The rate of development of the sex organs was much the same as for the birds who were kept outdoors in conditions of increased light.

This is an interesting theory, but it does not explain the migration of birds who spend the winter in the tropics where there is very little change in day length from season to season. And what about those that travel below the equator where seasons are reversed?

Not all birds migrate. Why are they not affected by food supply and changes in day length? Here are more mysteries about the built-in clocks of birds. Certainly, there is much to be learned about the clocks and the compasses which they use to make their journeys from one home to another.

5. Honeybees, Ants, and Wasps

Fortunately for men, the birds that fly over the roads in the sky are hungry birds which consume vast numbers of insects. Insects are man's greatest rival, for those which have not become meals for hungry birds consume vast quantities of the earth's food supply.

There may be several hundred million insects per acre of soil in many areas. And there may be between two and ten million different kinds of insects. Not all of them are harmful. Honeybees, for instance, are well known for the good that they do. They are also well known for their wonderful sense of time and direction.

Honeybees use their sense of time and direction when they get ready to swarm. And they show a wonderful sense of timing indeed.

There are three kinds of bees: queens who lay the eggs; workers, who are females that cannot lay eggs; and drones, who are the males which fertilize the eggs. There is only one queen to a hive. Drones are needed only when the queen makes her wedding flight and the eggs must be fertilized. When their part is done, and food is scarce, drones are starved or pushed out of the hive. Workers are busy day after day with special duties such as cleaning, feeding the young, feeding the queen, repairing and guarding the hive. Day after day the queen is busy laying eggs. She averages about 1,500 eggs per day in the summer; she may lay this many eggs summer after summer for several years, until she grows old and tired. Then a new queen must take her place. And males, or drones, must be raised to fertilize the eggs.

Since queens and drones develop at different rates, the eggs which develop into each must be laid at different times. The queen eggs are laid 17 days after the drone eggs. In this way, the drones will be ready

57

to fertilize a new queen's eggs at the proper time.

A second queen is needed, too, when a hive becomes crowded, for then some of the bees swarm with the old queen and the new one stays in the hive.

Suppose preparations have been made for swarming. A week before the great event, the scouts go out to find a new place for a hive. They fly long distances, investigating nooks and empty hives. They may choose natural homes or they may choose a hive which has been prepared by a beekeeper. The scouts report to the old hive and when the time is ready, the bees tumble out and gather together on a nearby branch. From this first settling place, a final group of scouts will make the decision of where the new home will be. Probably the scout whose choice has been selected leads the swarm to its new home, and here they build a new city within the next few months, for their sense of time makes them aware that they must prepare for the winter with a supply of honey and pollen. Once more the bees must work on a time schedule, for the young which are born early in spring must be fed from the winter supplies. From old home to new, time and direction are important.

Here is another example of bees using a sense of time: At certain times of the year, nectar flows in great amounts in the blossoms of trees and later in the flowers of white clover. Large amounts of nectar are needed to make honey for the winter's supply. When

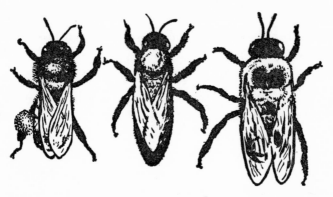

Left, worker bee with pollen basket on his rear leg. Center, young queen bee and, right, drone.

this flow of nectar is spotted by a bee, there is much excitement.

Imagine a huge field of white clover which is filled with nectar. The conditions are just right for the flow. The temperature is 70 degrees Fahrenheit, the air is moist and so is the soil. A bee has discovered this rich source of nectar ready for the gathering, but she cannot carry it to the hive alone. She must alert other workers and tell them where to come. To do this, she dances for them back at the hive. The dance is not just any kind, but a very special one which bees read just as carefully as a ship's navigator reads a compass.

Suppose the clover field is within a short distance, perhaps just 25 yards away. To show this, the dancing bee does a "round dance." She circles first to the right, then she reverses her direction and circles to the left. Round and round she goes for as long as a minute. Other bees join the dance and follow her around the circle. Still more bees gather round. The comb twinkles with dancing bees, and the excitement spreads. Suddenly the scout bee stops her dance and distributes drops of nectar to the others. Then the bees who have received the message fly from the hive in search of the nectar. They know what kind they are seeking because they have already had a sample. And they know that the flowers are nearby, for the dance was a "round dance."

Suppose the field of white clover is far away. If it is beyond 75 yards, the scout bee announces this information in a different kind of dance in which she gives the exact distance and the exact direction. Imagine a bee wagging her abdomen as she travels along a straight line. Now she turns to the left and makes a semicircle. She travels along the straight line again, wagging as she goes, and this time she makes a semicircle to the right. The whole dance is a figure-eight pattern with a straight line at the center. This means that the nectar is far away. But how far? The dance tells that too. The speed at which the bee dances along the straight line indicates exactly how far the honey is. Scientists with stop watches have learned to read the maps danced by bees. If the nectar is 100 yards away, the bee covers the distance of the straight line in a quarter of a minute. If the nectar is farther away, the bees travels more slowly. Of course, the worker bees who read the message have no stop watches. Still, many of them can read the message of the dance just as accurately as if they were timing it with a mechanical clock.

This explains how the bees know the distance of the rich source of the nectar, but how do they know the direction? The dance is a map which gives direction as well as distance. Bees have many-faceted eyes which see patterns in the sky even though it appears all blue to human beings. Each patch of the sky has a characteristic pattern which depends on the position of the sun. Even though the sun is completely hidden by clouds, bees know where the sun must be if they can see a small part of the sky. With this information, they can use the language of the dance to tell other bees the direction of the food. The sun is taken to be at the top of the comb. If the bee does her waggle dance from bottom to top, straight up the comb, the food must lie toward the sun. If the bee dances at an angle of 15 degrees to the right of the comb, the food will be at an angle of 15 degrees to the sun. If the dancer runs straight down on the waggle part of the figure-eight, she is indicating that nectar is in a direction opposite to that of the sun.

Experimenters have carefully observed these dances and have even made motion pictures of them for leisurely study. The Austrian scientist, Karl von Frisch, carried out many experiments from which he drew conclusions about the language of the bees.

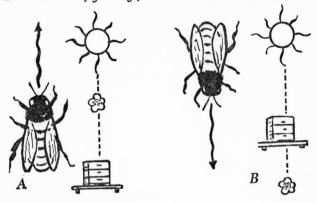

A *Bee runs up to show nectar is in direction of sun.*
B *Bees must fly away from sun to reach food.*

Even though this example of time and direction-finding is almost too amazing to believe, many other scientists have made observations and carried out experiments which indicate that he is correct.

Here is an experiment which was performed recently by a man who studies bees, Treat Davidson. It was done to test one of von Frisch's conclusions. Mr. Davidson placed two glasses of rich sugar syrup about 20 feet apart and about 50 feet from an observation hive. In one glass he added flavoring in the form of vanilla extract. The other glass of syrup was not flavored with the vanilla. Then he waited and watched to see what would happen.

The glasses of syrup were discovered at the same time by different scout bees who returned to the hive

C *Bees must fly at an angle of 60 degrees to right of sun to reach nectar.*

D *Nectar is at an angle of 120 degrees to right of sun.*

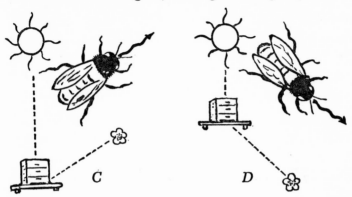

C   D

with the information that a rich source of food was nearby. The bee which visited the vanilla-flavored syrup was marked with red nail polish for identity. The sample which she gave to the workers at the end of her dance, and the pattern of her dance, led many workers to the dish. The supply of the better-tasting vanilla syrup was gone before less than half of the other syrup was carried to the hive. Certainly, the scout bee communicated the proper directions.

Many years ago men discovered that bees have a sense of time. A Swiss doctor, August Forel, had breakfast on his porch every morning at the same time. He noted that bees came to his table for sweets each day. They came at the regular time when the food was on the table, and they came at the same time when there was none. How did they know when it was his breakfast time?

Another scientist, von Buttel-Reepen, noted that bees exhibited a sense of time when collecting nectar from flowers. Buckwheat flowers secrete nectar each day about ten o'clock in the morning. At this time, hundreds of thousands of bees are busy collecting nectar. In the afternoon, even though the flowers smell and look the same, no bees visit the fields. When the nectar flows the next morning, the bees return. How do they know when ten o'clock has come?

As long as thirty years ago, Miss Ingeborg Beling, a student of Dr. von Frisch, worked out a method for studying the time sense of bees. Here is the way it is done. Twenty to thirty bees are marked with dots of color so that each can be identified. They are fed sugar water from a bowl at a feeding place for several days at the same time—between ten in the morning and noon. For the rest of the day, the bowl is kept empty. The bees are fed this way for six or eight days, then a test is made. A person sits next to the bowl on the test day and records every visit made by the bees. On this day, the bowl is kept empty all day long. Such tests show that bees can be trained so that they know the exact time when there is usually sugar water in the bowl. On the test day they search and search for sugar water, but when the regular feeding time ends, fewer bees come to the bowl. After a half hour, the feeding station is empty.

Eggs, larvae, pupa and adult honeybee

Could it be that the bees come to the feeding station at such regular intervals because they have developed a hunger rhythm? Scientists say not, because the bees do not use the sugar water directly. They fill their honey bags with it, return to the hive, and give up the sugar water to other bees who store it where it can be used later for making honey. Collector bees eat when they are not collecting, whenever they are hungry.

How do the bees know what time it is? Do they tell time in this case by the position of the sun? To find this out, scientists took the bees into a special room where the temperature was kept constant and the room was lighted in exactly the same way during the day and night. Even though a man might lose all sense of time in such a place, the bees came at the proper hour for their feeding.

Later, bees were taken to the gallery of a salt mine, located about 600 feet below the surface of the earth, where factors such as cosmic rays and the capacity of the air to conduct electricity might have no effect. At the earth's surface, both of these factors have daily rhythms. If these factors are eliminated it would seem that the bees could not use them to set their clocks, for they were trained to visit the bowl of sugar water just as they were trained in the bee room and at other places on the earth's surface.

The clocks of bees depend on a twenty-four-hour schedule. When attempts were made to train them at different intervals, bees did not learn the way they do on a regular twenty-four-hour pattern. But do they use a built-in clock or is there some outside factor on which they depend? This question was the reason for some very interesting experiments. In one of these, a hive of bees was carried across the ocean by plane. Dr. Max Renner, of the University of Munich, first tackled the question of whether changes in the speed at which bees use their own energy had an influence on their sense of time. Bees were late at the feeding table when they were kept in a refrigerator after the last training period. This coldness slowed the rate at which their bodies used food—their rate of metabolism —and upset the built-in clocks. But attempts to speed up metabolism by drugs, and thus bring bees to the sugar water ahead of schedule, did not succeed. From the refrigerator experiments it seemed clear that the time sense depends on some action in the bee's body, but could this action be determined by something outside? The question was still not answered.

Suppose the bees depend on the twenty-four-hour turning of the earth. How could this be determined? It was in this experiment that Dr. Renner carried bees from Paris to New York. There is a difference of five hours in the time of these two cities. When it is 8:15 in the evening in Paris, it is only 3:15 in the afternoon in New York. If the bees were influenced by the turning of the earth, they would feed twenty-nine hours later instead of the usual twenty-four hours when moved from Paris to New York.

Dr. Renner trained bees to feed in a bee room between 8:15 and 10:15 in the evening in Paris. Then he packed them in a traveling case and checked them at the Paris airport with his luggage. The bees went with him across the ocean, and twenty hours later they were put in a bee room in the American Museum of Natural History in New York City. The bee room was exactly like the one in which they were trained in Paris. Lights were kept on constantly in both rooms, so the natural night and day did not enter into the problem. Would they still be on Paris time? Or would some external influence bring them to the sugar water bowl on New York time? Dr. Renner, other scientists, and many other interested people waited to see what the bees would do. There was even some question as to whether or not the bees would go to the bowl at any time, for their sense of time and location might have been disturbed by the long voyage over the ocean.

The bees came. And they came on schedule—on Paris schedule. Nothing in the sky or in the position of the earth changed their regular twenty-four-hour feeding rhythm. To some, this experiment seemed to show clearly that bees have an internal clock, a sense of time governed by their own bodies. But others still question whether or not some cosmic force influences rhythm in animals.

ANTS

Some ants are strange navigators. Their built-in compasses depend on highly developed senses. They can smell extremely faint odors, and they can recognize chemicals by their sense of touch. Perhaps you have watched ants tapping food with their antennae. By doing this, they can find their way in the darkness using chemicals as a guide.

Have you ever watched trails of ants? Perhaps you have interrupted the trail with a stick to find out what the ants would do. If you were to place a colony of ants at one end of a table and a pile of sugar at the other, they would travel over a straight path, back and forth, carrying the sugar to the colony. Suppose you interrupted the path by rubbing your finger in front of a sugar-carrying ant. The ant stops, waves its feelers around, and taps them on the table. Then ants crowd on both sides of the place where you rubbed your finger. Some run back and forth from the nest to

There are over 2,500 species of ants.

this place; others run back and forth from the sugar to this place. Then a few investigate by running over the place. They meet other ants on the other side of the line and the trail is continued once more. By rubbing your finger across the path, you destroyed the trail of chemicals which the ants smelled as they traveled back and forth. If you had rubbed a piece of cotton across the path instead of your finger, you would probably have found that the trail was not interrupted. The chemicals left behind by the rubbing of the finger confuse the ants, while there are none left by the cotton to upset them.

Some kinds of ants lay trails by leaving a drop of material from their intestines from time to time as they move along. The marks have a shape and point in the direction in which the ants are going. But no one knows whether or not ants can recognize a trail by these spots. They seem to follow a trail by tapping antennae on the ground instead of feeling each spot.

69

The chemicals which mark most ant trails last only for a short time, perhaps only minutes or hours, but there are some which may last for as long as a month. These are the trails of the Army ants which live in the tropical regions of Central and South America, and in Africa. These insects are totally blind, so their trails are especially important. Army ants have no permanent homes but spend their days wandering over the jungles in search of food. They travel in long columns, keeping in touch with each other by their senses of smell and touch. They are swift and fierce, exploring everything in their paths. They eat chickens, rats, snakes, other insects, and even attack human beings. Marching columns of ants cause every living thing in their paths to flee or be eaten.

Each ant in the marching column is guided by the chemicals of other ants in the trail. The front of the column explores new territory a little at a time, then returns to the old familiar odors.

Each evening the columns of marching ants turn back and gather together in a nest of hundreds of thousands, forming a mass of ants with the queen and her young protected in the center. When dawn comes, marching columns go forth again in search of food and at night a nest may be made in the old location or in an advance area where there is a better food supply.

Sometimes the Army ants stay in the same place for a few days while the queen lays eggs and the eggs develop into larvae. Then workers carry the larvae gingerly in their jaws as they march along. Larvae grow into pupae. During another resting period, pupae become adults ready to join the march as working ants.

Eggs, larvae, pupa and black worker ant

Both ants and honeybees are experts in finding their way. Some ants, just like bees, can recognize patterns in the sky and guide themselves by these patterns. But the ants do not tell other ants where food is located by a dance; they use quick movements and bring up from their storage sacs the food which they have found.

THE BEE WOLF, A WASP NAVIGATOR

There is a kind of wasp which brings home to its young nothing but honeybees for dinner. This wasp, known scientifically as Philanthus triangulum Fabr., and commonly as a bee wolf, has an amazing ability by which it finds its solitary home. And it has the ability to recognize a honeybee among the many other kinds of insects. This bee wolf was the subject of detailed studies made by a Dutch zoologist, Niko Tinbergen, and his associates.

Imagine a stretch of sand in the central part of Holland where these bee wolves dig nests for their eggs.

They shovel out the sand with their hind legs so that there is a shaft underground which may be as long as 2 feet. At the end, there may be from one to five cells for eggs which will develop into larvae. Each hungry larvae will have its own supply of honeybees. In finding this food and in bringing it to the proper home, bee wolves make use of their built-in compasses.

Dr. Tinbergen first established that each wasp came back to her own nest, not just to any burrow in the sand. He caught wasps and marked them with dots of colored paint. Then he released them so that they could go about their work of constructing nests and searching for bees. Soon after the wasps were marked, they flew away on their missions. But each one followed a pattern at take-off. Each flew in circles over her burrow for a while as if she were taking a good look at the surroundings so that she could recognize them on returning. The wasps then flew to a heath area about a half mile away, where many bees were buzzing about. Each wasp captured a bee and returned home with the dead insect for her nest.

Imagine a wasp winging her way through the air with a bee carried in an upside down position beneath her and held in place with the wasp's middle pair of legs. She flies directly to her own nest in the ground, deposits the dead bee inside, and goes forth for another one. Some wasps make several trips to the hunting grounds in one afternoon, but each returns to the proper nest every time.

How does a bee wolf find its own nest among the many burrows which have been dug in the sand? This is exactly what Dr. Tinbergen set out to learn. He did this by trying to confuse a wasp. He mixed up the landmarks. In some experiments he placed regular landmarks, such as a circle of pine cones, around a burrow while a wasp was working inside. After coming out, she carefully covered the hole with sand, and seemed to observe the pine cones as she looped above them. When she came back, the pine cones were carefully arranged in a similar circle, but not around the nest. This was the work of the scientist who was testing the wasp. The wasp proceeded toward the pine cones, but when she was about 4 feet above the ground, she suddenly stopped and acted very strangely. She flew up again, circling around in the air, much disturbed. She finally began to search low over the sand, dug in several places, and finally dropped the bee she was carrying. After twenty-five minutes of searching, the wasp came upon the nest as if by accident. Then she picked up the bee and dragged it in.

Such experiments with pine cones and other objects led Dr. Tinbergen to believe that wasps get their bearings from landmarks before flying out to hunt bees. They may travel a mile or so, but they return to their own nests using vision for their navigation.

How are wasps able to differentiate honeybees (the insects which they bring home) from other bees and insects? There are many that resemble honey-

Hover fly

bees. One, a hover fly, mimics honeybees so well that even birds are confused. But wasps always find the honeybees; they never choose a hover fly. Dr. Tinbergen discovered why. He watched bee wolves recovering bees which they had dropped, and he noticed that they always approached the lost insects against the wind. This led him to believe that the bee's scent was carried by the wind and recognized by the wasp.

Wasps seize bees only after their antennae touch the bees. Then the wasps quickly swing around until they are facing the bees and drive their stings into the bees' chins. Since antennae contain organs of smell as well as touch, this is further evidence that smell might be involved.

74

Tests showed that wasps inspect any object about the size of a honeybee. After coming fairly close, the wasps depend on their sense of smell for recognition. So both sight and smell play a part in aiding the wasps to identify bees. And certainly sight helps to bring the hunter home with her feast of honeybees for the hungry larvae which will hatch from the eggs in the underground nests.

There are many other kinds of wasps besides the bee-killers which have interesting built-in compasses, but perhaps none are more amazing than those of the bee-wolf wasps.

Bee wolf stinging a bee

Convergent ladybird,
or ladybeetle

6. More Insect Mysteries

Many other kinds of insects make use of built-in clocks and compasses. Sometimes insect life depends on getting ready for winter at the right time. In such a case, the alarm clock may be light.

LIGHT SETS THE CLOCK

Light has provided a promising clue in the riddle of what controls the built-in clocks of animals. At any place on the earth, the number of daylight hours is determined by the season of the year, with a gradual change from day to day. In the Northern Hemisphere from December 21 until June 21, the days grow longer. For the next six months, until December 21 comes again, the days grow shorter. In the Southern Hemisphere, just the opposite is true. This change in day length is a sort of natural alarm clock which helps plants and animals to prepare for the coming season. For instance, many insects prepare for winter before the end of the summer. They do this because of the changing length of day, because light sets the clock.

To find out more about the effect of day length on insects, Dr. Albert Beck of the University of Wisconsin has reared insects in an incubator where there are artificial days. The European corn borer is an insect which was especially interesting in these experiments. When a batch was reared on days with twelve hours of light and twelve hours of darkness, all of the corn borers hibernated. But when Dr. Beck gave corn borers days that were six hours long, followed by nights that were six hours long, none of these insects hibernated. Dr. Beck believes that a "day" of at least eight hours is necessary to bring about hibernation.

Each twenty-four-hour day involves one change from light to dark. Something about this change is the switch that sets the animal clock. The clock measures the amount of time between dark and dark, or the length of the day. Assuming that there is some mechanism that determines the length of day, Dr. Beck is trying to find out what it is in the insect's body that times the day.

Where the winters grow too cold for insect activity, preparations are made for the insect to spend the winter in a form that is protected. An adult praying mantis cannot live through the winter. Praying mantis eggs are laid in the late summer or early fall in

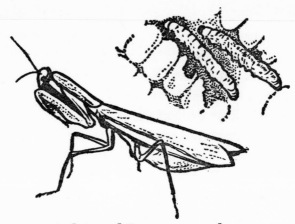

Praying mantis, left, and European corn borer

clusters on the branches of trees and shrubs. They are deposited in a foamy mass which hardens when exposed to the air and which protects them from the cold winter weather. Perhaps it is the shortening of day length which tells the praying mantis that it is time to lay the eggs which unlike her can survive the winter. Some other kinds of insects winter over in the egg form, too, while still others spend the winter as larvae. Some hibernate in the form of pupa, and others winter as adults.

LADY BEETLES

Here is an insect which sleeps during the winter in adult form. Some kinds of lady beetles, or ladybird beetles, are known to travel long distances to spend the summer or the winter in a different place.

Scientists who experimented with one kind did not take into account their built-in clocks and compasses. This kind is the convergent lady beetle, so called because two white dashes on its back almost meet, or converge. You can recognize this variety by the white dashes and black dots on the orange wing covers. There are an equal number of dots on each side and one dot near the head. Thousands upon thousands of convergent lady beetles attack green flies along certain parts of the coast of California. In doing so they help farmers a great deal, for green flies feed on crops and fruit trees.

Lady beetles feed on the green flies in the summer. In the autumn they gather together high in the hills, and they spend the winter under stones or among dead leaves or even in open spots on the hillsides. When spring comes, the lady beetles wake up and fly back to the valley where they feed on the green flies during the following summer.

Scientists collected lady beetles and kept them in cold storage during the winter. In the spring, they released the insects in areas where there were many green flies. But ladybirds fly far when they awaken in the spring. And the ones in cold storage did not know that they did not have a trip to make. Marked lady beetles soon flew far from the area where they were liberated. Perhaps they were trying to fly the hundred miles back to the valley from the hills. Where they went, no one knows. But scientists do know that the lady beetles did not stay around to eat the local green flies.

Most kinds of insects hibernate in some form during the winter, but some travel far from the cold winters of their summer homes, seeking warmer skies in the south. One of the most common butterflies in the United States is a famous traveler. This kind, the Monarch, or Milkweed, lives all over the United States. You may have seen its orange and black wings. Many travel from Canada to Florida, while those in the west travel to particular trees in California.

Have you ever seen a butterfly tree? About 60 miles south of San Francisco, in Pacific Grove, California, there are trees which are the winter homes for thousands of Monarch butterflies. These same trees have been used year after year for over sixty years by the winter visitors. The butterflies sleep there for most of the winter, but now and then, on a bright sunny day, some will fly about. They make quite a sight for tourists.

Thoughtless people have sometimes thrown stones at the butterflies to see them fly in a large group from the trees. So the people who live in Pacific Grove passed laws to prevent this, and now the butterflies sleep undisturbed.

In the spring the butterflies are more active. They leave the trees more frequently on short trips. One by one, they leave the trees forever and journey north until some reach as far as southern Canada about two months later. On the way north, the female butterflies lay eggs on young milkweed plants which are just coming above the ground. After they lay their eggs they die. But the eggs develop into caterpillars and butterflies emerge from them in mid-summer. By the end of the summer, the new generation of Monarch butterflies is ready to fly south to the butterfly trees where they will sleep for most of the winter. Butterflies gather in flocks and travel in long lines on sunny days, stopping to rest on the way. Some must travel a thousand miles in order that they may reach the butterfly trees.

The children and, in some cases, the grandchildren of the butterflies that were there last year fill the trees. Then they will go north in the spring and lay more eggs which will grow into butterflies that will fill the trees the next year. No one knows how the butterflies find the trees. No one knows what tells them to fly south at the proper time.

Butterflies take many different paths across the world. Each kind follows its own pattern. There are records of thousands of butterflies crossing lakes, flying up mountains, and winging over plains. One time a whole island was covered with white fluttering wings when migrating butterflies were caught on the sticky leaves of the sundew plants that grew there. Each plant captured about four to seven butterflies, and there were so many plants on the island that the total count of butterflies was about 6 million insects.

Wind and rain, too, take their toll of butterflies—sometimes sudden storms drive butterflies into the waters of lakes during their migration. But in spite of the hazards, many kinds of butterflies take regular journeys at certain times of the year to definite places.

Many different people help to gather records of masses of butterflies in flight. One weatherman, Mr. P. H. Smythe of Montgomery, Alabama, watched the travels of the Clouded Sulfur butterflies as they passed across the park in front of his window between the end of July each year until the end of November, traveling in a southeasterly direction. Fewer butterflies traveled in the opposite direction between the spring months of March and April. These butterflies must have laid their eggs in the spring in order for so many insects to have joined the flight in the late summer and fall.

One report tells of "Snout" butterflies which spread

Clouded Sulfur butterfly, left,
and "Snout" butterfly

across 250 miles of Texas with about a million and a quarter of them passing by each minute.

Some butterflies and moths migrate in caterpillar form. Processionary caterpillars are strange migratory animals. They travel in a procession in which each animal is linked to its neighbor by tiny threads. The leaders are followed, no matter where they go. Sometimes they accidentally get behind the last caterpillar in the group, and thus a ring is formed. The caterpillars travel in a circle, on and on, until they die of exhaustion or are accidentally separated.

For many years, insects known as "cotton worms," the larval stage of a cotton moth, did serious damage to fields of cotton in the southern part of the United States. They appeared mysteriously in June, and generation after generation of these caterpillars kept eating the leaves of plants, until the end of summer when the cotton season was over. Then the insects disappeared as mysteriously as they had come. Where did they come from? Where did they go? Now it is known that this cotton moth is a pest in parts of South America when it is not feeding on the cotton plants of the United States. Adult moths come to the United States through Mexico and perhaps across the Caribbean Sea. Here they lay eggs which produce caterpillars that feed on the leaves of cotton plants.

Here is a strange ending to the story of the cotton moth's flight. Instead of going south at the end of the summer, masses of cotton moths fly north. One year there were so many in the railway station in Jersey City, New Jersey, that they had to be swept into buckets after they were killed. Many others have been seen flying around lights in cities such as Washington, Philadelphia, New York, and Boston. These cities are hundreds of miles from the cotton belt. No one knows why the moths travel so far north.

Countless numbers of butterflies and moths travel from place to place day and night. Some fly in a mass far out to sea, where they fall into the waves and die. In this way, new species may reach islands and distant coasts of a mainland, but most mass migrations perish. There are many records of mass movements of butterflies in a definite direction in every continent but Antarctica. Some have been noticed year after year at the same season moving in the same direction. But many records are incomplete, and there is much to be learned about these strange journeys. What meanings do these movements have? Why do butterflies and moths fly in a definite direction? What acts as a clock for those who travel year after year at the same time? Light may set the clock which provides them with information about changing seasons, but something inside of these butterflies and moths reacts to the changing day length.

LOCUSTS

Locusts don't make a round-trip journey the way Monarch butterflies do, but they are famous travelers.

Plagues of locusts have been known for many years. You may have first heard of one when reading the Bible, since a plague of locusts is described in the book of Exodus. At the end of the plague "there remained not any green thing, either tree or herb of the field, through all the land of Egypt." The locusts are described as being brought by the east wind and as being driven into the Red Sea by a strong west wind. In recent years, 3,000 years after the Book of Exodus was written, scientists have begun investigating the connection between wind direction and the flight of locusts. They still do not know all the answers.

Imagine looking into the sky at a brown cloud. You may look at it more closely through your field glasses and find that the cloud is made of thousands of locusts moving in the direction of the wind. They come close and fly lower to the ground. Soon they cover your garden, where they eat and eat until not a speck of green is left. They cover the trees and the houses and the cars. When a car on which they have settled begins to move, the insects rise up like a huge spray. Some get inside the driver's shirt. Some get in his mouth when he opens it to talk. All around, the locusts eat, destroying every green living thing. Then they fly away with the wind.

Locusts are a certain kind of short-horned grasshopper. In certain years, when moisture conditions are exactly right for grasshoppers, huge numbers hatch. These insects are unusually active and a slightly dif-

*Millions of locusts may
travel together in a swarm.*

ferent color from those of normal years. When they
grow up and get their wings, these locusts form a mass
and fly away together. Some travel more than a thousand miles from their breeding grounds. This mass
migration usually occurs in tropical and subtropical
dry areas of the world. Locusts cover the sky and the
earth, some breaking rather large branches of trees
with their weight as they land. It is almost impossible
to imagine over ten thousand million grasshoppers,
each 6 inches long, flying over an area a mile wide, at
a speed of about 6 miles per hour. Such a swarm has
been recorded as lasting for nine hours. After that, not
one locust was to be seen.

Long ago, many people died of starvation after a
locust invasion. A ton of locusts can eat 10 tons of
vegetation, and a swarm may consist of 43 billion tons
of locusts. Even today, there are local famines because of them. But in many areas, modern chemicals
are being sprayed into the air to kill these insects.

What makes the locusts travel in such large groups,
and all in the same direction? Scientists believe that

locust movements do not necessarily follow a regular pattern to and from different home areas at different seasons of the year as bird migrations do; however, they have some kind of a built-in clock and built-in compass which directs them to swarm.

COCKROACHES

Among the many different kinds of insects that at some time or other are driven by a furious impulse to move from place to place are the cockroaches. At times, great marches of these insects take place, but they usually occur at night and are seldom seen. But large numbers of cockroaches have been tagged with radioactive atoms, which are chemicals that emit rays. These rays will produce a clicking sound whenever an instrument known as a Geiger counter is nearby. When these chemicals are injected into cockroaches, their travels can be checked. For instance, if some cockroaches in Washington are tagged with radioactive chemicals and are found 50 miles away where no insects have been tagged, one knows that the cockroaches have managed to travel that distance. Since they travel in large groups, a few radioactive insects can give information about large numbers.

One report about a cockroach "march" describes thousands of these insects walking from the rear of a restaurant and moving directly across a muddy street to a building on the opposite side. No one knows exactly why the group decided it was time to move to another home. Perhaps there was not enough food in the old home and the pressure of overpopulation drove them on. But what set the clock—what triggered the exact time of the move?

One of the largest mass migrations on record was observed by the famous naturalist, William Beebe, and his staff. When they were making studies in a narrow pass in Venezuela, billions of all kinds of insects flew south through the path. The great flight continued day and night from May through September. No one ever saw these great masses of insects return through the pass, and no one knows what caused the huge mass migration to the south. It is another of the many riddles about insect clocks and compasses.

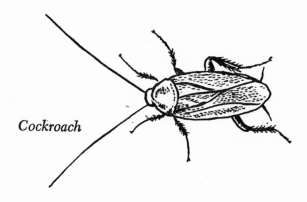

Cockroach

Female fur seal

7. Mammals on the Move

Most people think of mammals when they think of animals. Mammals are animals whose young are born in an immature condition and are fed from the mammary glands of the mother. There are about 4,000 kinds of mammals, all of whom have hair and maintain a constant body temperature. Only a few of these 4,000 kinds of mammals have internal clocks and compasses which direct motion of the kind described in previous chapters. Few mammals migrate, but those who do are interesting ones.

FUR SEALS

The fur seals of the Pacific spend most of the year in the open sea. The large male animals, or bulls, live together in one area of the sea while the females and young seals travel farther from their homes. The females and their young tumble about in the sea and play near the surface of the water as far south as California, but they do not come near the coast. When spring comes, their internal clocks and compasses are set for a journey to the breeding grounds. Alaskan fur seals travel several thousand miles through the sea with an unerring certainty that brings them to passages in the Aleutian Islands. They travel through these passages to the Pribilof Islands about 100 miles beyond. These islands are small and often fog-bound, but the seals find them year after year.

First come the bulls. They arrive early in May and climb up the beaches where each one stakes out his territory of several square yards. He defends this area against all who come near. The largest and strongest bulls choose the most desirable sites which are located nearest the water's edge, but first there is a great deal of fighting. Once they have claimed them, the bulls do not leave their territories for food or water, and they get little chance to sleep. Each one must be constantly on guard so that another bull does not take his area. Each beachmaster, as the bull is called, is at least seven years old. He may live as long as twenty years and weigh from 450 to 600 pounds.

A month or so after the bulls arrive, the gentle cow seals reach the beach. They are only about one-fifth as large as the bulls. Each bull tries to get as many cows as he can for his own harem, so there is much coaxing of the females and quarreling with other males. The number of cows which a bull acquires varies between 1 and 100. Bachelor bulls, or young males, gather in groups apart from the harem areas, or spend their time along the edge of the beach ready to take the harem of a bull who lets down his guard.

Several days after the pregnant seals arrive, the young pups are born. Each mother nurses only her own, which she recognizes among hundreds of others. If a mother seal is killed, her newborn pup starves to death. The cows go to the water for fish, and the young seals soon go down to play and learn to swim.

In the fall, the bulls are the first to leave the colony. They are exhausted from lack of food and rest, and they head for the abundant food of the open sea. By the end of the year, all the fur seals have left their beaches. They will stay in the ocean until early in the spring, when their built-in clocks and compasses lead them back to the islands again.

At the opposite end of the earth, Southern fur seals migrate in much the same way, with the males arriving first and taking up their territories. The females come later and give birth to their young soon after arrival. In both Northern and Southern fur seals, the young, which have been developing inside the females, are born almost as soon as the females arrive. Sometimes it is just a few hours later. If their internal clocks and compasses did not lead them home at exactly the right time, the young would be born at sea and drown.

Several kinds of sea lions and seals make migrations similar to those of the fur seals. Sometimes the surface of the sea seems covered with immense herds of animals which have assembled during the breeding season to give birth to their young on the floating cakes of ice.

WHALES

Sometimes thousands of migrating whales can be seen as they pass the coasts. In California there is a station which counts gray whales as they pass this coast twice a year. These whales bear their young in the warm waters during the winter season and go north again for the summer. Young whales are born at sea in a more advanced state than that of the fur seals and are able to swim beside their mothers at once.

The annual migration of whales, like those of other animals, is closely tied to feeding and reproduction. Their built-in clocks and compasses lead them to places where the food supply is greatest in one season and where breeding conditions are best in another season. Unlike seals and many other animals, whalebone whales go to colder regions to find food. Whalebone whales are those which have sievelike fringes of the jaws called baleen plates. They live entirely on minute plants and animals, known as plankton, which are found on the surface of the sea. There may be millions of these plants and animals in a cubic inch of water —so many that they give a characteristic green color to the area of the ocean where they are so plentiful. Plankton grows abundantly in the cold waters of the polar seas where there are long hours of daylight. Recently, a ring of concentrated ocean life, thousands of miles in diameter, has been discovered around Antarctica. Here there is fourteen times as much plankton as in tropical waters. Here is a feast for the hungry whales, who strain this plankton through the thin, flexible baleen plates which replace their teeth. The plates are somewhat like venetian blinds, with a fringe on the inner edge that forms a sort of hair mat to capture food. A whalebone whale opens his mouth at the surface of the ocean as widely as possible and allows the water to flow in. Then he closes his mouth and puts his tongue at the roof so that water is forced

Whalebone, or Baleen, whales.

through the thick hair-like fringe on the baleen plates. In this way, the plants and animals are strained out and held on the surface of the fringes. The whale closes his mouth and lowers his tongue to the floor of his mouth. The baleen plates straighten out and the plants and animals are jerked off the fringes onto his tongue. The whale quickly swallows them, millions at a time.

When the ice sheet extends farther south with the coming of winter, and the plankton of the polar seas is no longer available, the whales set out for warmer waters where their young are born.

There are many paths taken by different kinds of whales. For instance, the Blue Whales bear their young when it is spring in the North Atlantic near Norway, Iceland, and eastern Greenland. After this, they travel south all the way to the bottom of the world, sometimes encircling the Antarctic continent. They reach the North Atlantic again in the next year in time to bear their young at the accustomed breeding grounds. Sperm whales travel from the North Pacific Ocean to the South Atlantic and back each year, rounding the tip of Africa when it is summer there.

In an effort to learn more about the migration of whales, metal markers have been shot into the blubber of thousands of them. Some were found 2,500 miles from the place where the numbered, metal arrows were shot into them ten years before.

Whales, even though they must come to the surface to breathe, can stay under the water for long periods of time, for they have tremendous lungs. They even swim under arctic ice that is 2 feet thick and burst through it when they need to breathe. It is believed that sometimes the surfacing is a navigational aid. Sometimes whales thrust their heads far out of the water, almost seeming to stand on their tails, and they seem to use their eyes to observe their positions in relation to the coast. They also may use vibrations in the water which people cannot hear, to check the depth or the position of an underwater landmark. They can make these high-pitched sounds by shuddering their huge diaphragms which sets air in motion in their tremendous lungs. The vibrations pass out into the surrounding water and come back to them as echoes.

No matter how whales find their way, it is certain that they can reach the same breeding grounds year after year at the proper time. And their routes are carefully studied by the men who harpoon them for the valuable products which they yield. There are laws which protect whales today so that the supply will not become depleted. A treaty was signed by the nations which engage in whaling. Each nation is represented on the International Whaling Commission which makes laws to regulate the number of whales that can be killed. It is estimated that there are only a few hundred thousand whales left in the entire world.

Laws came almost too late to protect another mammal which once migrated in tremendous numbers in the western part of the United States and Canada. Great herds of American bison, often called buffalo, roamed over thousands of square miles. There were as many as 75 million animals. Today the thousands that remain still migrate between the north and south, but they are no longer the great sight that they used to be. Today most of these animals are found in government parks and reservations.

Great herds of caribou, or American reindeer, move southward in the autumn and northward in the spring for several hundred miles in the northwestern part of

Indian elephant with small ears;
African elephant in background

Canada. Farther south, American elk, or wapiti, answer the call of their built-in clocks to move from

Above, American bison
Center, American elk, or wapiti
Bottom, caribou

place to place. At the end of the summer, female wapiti leave the high mountain pastures and go down to the sheltered valleys. Next come the young males, who are followed by the bulls. But as soon as the snow begins to melt, the males start back to the mountain pastures, and the females follow, taking along the newborn calves. Year after year, the wapiti follow the same pattern.

Far away from the wapiti, elephants follow a seasonal migration both in India and Africa. According to African natives, elephants seek the shelter of forests in the summer, and stay in the open country during the rainy season so that they are not annoyed by the constant drip which falls from the trees. Some herds of elephants follow the same path year after year at the same time of each year. Other herds take a long time for their journeys. One kind of elephant takes a well-marked route for breeding purposes, which covers a total distance of about 400 miles during a period of three years.

BATS

Large mammals are not the only kind that migrate. Bats are mouse-like creatures that have wings and fly at night. Although many bats hibernate, there are some which travel from one place to another, according to the season. Some bats migrate a hundred miles or more from their summer range to the cave where they hibernate. The hoary bat is a tree bat that goes south to the Gulf States for the winter and spends its summer in the northern part of the United States and Canada. Other kinds, too, make annual trips, but many of their habits are still unknown and not understood.

For instance, no one knows why some bats live in a certain cave in the cold months and move out in the spring even though the temperature inside the cave varies only a few degrees during the whole year. When the winter bats move out, other kinds of bats move in and take their places on the roof and walls.

Tags are placed on many bats in an effort to learn more about their movements. In one method, tags are fastened to young bats. These metal markers stay in place for the rest of each bat's life and, since they are put on the wings, they are more easily seen than leg bands. This helps scientists to follow their travels and to know when their clocks are set for migration.

Bats are famous for their built-in compasses. Both the varieties that migrate and those that sleep through the winter can find their way through dense forest in complete darkness. Hundreds can fly through passageways without bumping into one another or into the walls of a cave. It has been known for many years that bats can fly safely in the dark or with their eyes covered. Long ago in Italy, Abbé Spallanzani, suspected that bats did not depend on sight to find their way and to catch food. Toward the end of the eighteenth century he blinded some bats and released them in a room in which there were numerous strings. The bats avoided the strings as well as when they could see. Spallanzani also released some of the blinded bats outdoors and caught them early in the morning four days later. He dissected them and found that their stomach were full of insects, showing that these blinded bats were still able to find and catch their food. Spallanzani made another important discovery. He found that bats collided with obstacles when their ears were closed, but he could not explain how their built-in compasses worked.

Not until 1920 did men begin to understand that bats found their way by emitting sounds too high for the human ear to hear. And it was twenty years later that Dr. Donald Griffin and Dr. Robert Galambos at Harvard University solved the riddle of bat navigation. They used an electronic apparatus that detected sound outside the range which humans hear and found that bats were giving off sounds in this range. By hearing the echoes of the sounds, bats can find their way in total darkness. These scientists then blindfolded some bats and found that they could avoid obstacles. Then they plugged their ears and found that the bats collided with obstacles. When one ear was plugged, a bat did better than when both ears were, but still it bumped against small targets and wires. In another experiment, the scientists covered the mouths of the bats but kept the ears free. The bats had just as much trouble as when their ears were plugged. This prevented the emission of the high sounds, so the bats lost their ability to navigate.

The sounds which bats make are not totally out of the range of human ears, although most all of them are. When bats emit a cry, you might hear a faint tick with very careful listening. It is difficult to hear it because of the noise of the fluttering wings. You must stand very close to the flying bat, something that many people cannot do without making a noise themselves, for it is tempting to squeal even though one knows that the bats will not fly in one's hair. But if you listen carefully you can hear a tick that is somewhat like the tick of a wristwatch.

If a bat heard its own squeaks when it made them, it would not be able to hear the echo. Each squeak lasts only a fraction of a thousandth of a second. Some scientists believe that when the squeak is made, small muscles in the bat's ear act in such a way that the bat does not hear the cry. The ear is ready immediately afterward to hear the echo. Sometimes a bat emits as many as fifty cries in a single second.

Further experiments showed that when there are difficult obstacles, such as many wires strung across a room, bats emit cries in very rapid succession. If the path is clear, the rate is lower. Their system cannot be jammed the way radar can. Bats still find their way even when there is much noise in a room. They can hear echoes which are about two thousand times fainter than other sounds that are being made.

Bats, radar and sonar use the location of echoes, a method known as echolocation. Of course, radar uses radio waves, while bats and sonar use sound waves. Sonar locates objects in water by generating sounds in the ocean and locating the echo which comes back from a fish, a submarine, or the bottom of the sea. Electronic engineers may learn to improve sonar by studying the skills of bats.

Porpoises, too, use echolocation, and they are being studied in an effort to learn more about this kind of navigation under water. Kathy, for example, is a porpoise who swims over an obstacle course in a large aquarium. She has traveled through an underwater maze over 200 times without hitting an obstacle even though the twisting pattern was changed for each performance. She can even travel the course blindfolded, for, like the bats, she finds her way by appraising echoes of the sounds she makes. From these, she can judge distance perfectly. Kathy is not performing as an entertainer; she is part of a U.S. Navy experiment which has been conducted to learn more about echo-location.

Blind people use echolocation when they tap their canes on the floor and listen to the echoes which come back to them. Dr. Donald R. Griffin, whose work on bat echolocation has been extensive, hopes that the bats' system of navigation may be a basis for perfecting a guide system for blind people. Many blind people have already developed the ability to orient themselves in a room by the use of echoes. They walk down busy streets, turn corners and avoid obstacles by using echoes as a guide; for man, too, has a sort of built-in compass which seems to improve with use.

Porpoises

The built-in compasses of bats and men serve a purpose which is easily understood. Some built-in compasses lead animals in a certain direction of march that results only in death. This is true of the springbucks and lemmings.

Springbucks are antelopes which resemble gazelles in build and appearance. They leap high into the air somewhat like a bucking horse; this is why they are called springbucks. Such an animal can make a series of great leaps, rising 8 to 10 feet in the air again and again with great grace.

At one time there were countless thousands of springbucks in South Africa, where they roamed over vast plains and desert land. They are probably still the most common kind of antelope in that part of the country. From time to time, between ten to twenty years, springbucks increase greatly in number. They are normally shy, but when these great increases in population occur they change character and become bold. At such times they mass together for a great migration. Then springbucks do not seem to be afraid of human beings at all. Thousands march together through villages, work their way up mountains and down to the beaches, traveling in almost a straight line. Like the locusts, they eat everything green that is in their path. They march on and on for many miles until they reach the edge of the sea. Then the springbucks plunge into the water and swim on until they

Springbuck

drown. Only those that remain behind in the desert live to become the parents of future generations of springbucks.

What sets the clock for the migration of springbucks? Scientists believe that these mass migrations are due partly to overpopulation. Climate plays a part, too, for the springbucks may be making their march in search of more drinking water. No matter what the reason, there are times when huge numbers leave their desert homes, never to return.

Lemmings are famous for their death marches, too. These animals are yellowish-brown with short stubby tails. They look somewhat like hamsters, and they are closely related to hamsters and rats. Lemmings live in the highlands of Norway and Sweden and are normally timid creatures. For years they live peacefully, making their nests of straw and lining them with hair. In the nests, from three to eight little lemmings begin their lives. Lemming families have two broods of young each year, so it is easy to see that the number of animals increase rapidly. Foxes, wolves, dogs and other animals eat some of them and usually keep the number down. But now and then, sometimes every four, five, or ten years, the lemmings become unusually plentiful. There are so many of them that food is scarce and the animals become restless. Then armies of the lemmings gather together and hundreds of thousands come down from their homes in the mountains. They begin a march toward the sea, eating grass and nibbling at the young plants as they go. Nothing stops them. They travel over fields, through barns, across streams, ponds, and lakes, always toward the sea. The lemmings go on and on, causing great damage to crops, for there are so many of them. If a haystack is in their path, they gnaw right through it. The march of the lemmings is a terrible sight. Thousands of animals die from hunger and disease along the way; some kill each other in fights, and others become food for birds and beasts. But the march goes on, for the urge to drive ahead is strong. At last they come to the edge of the sea. Even this does not stop them. The thousands of lemmings that are left plunge into the sea and swim. They swim on until they drown.

Not all lemmings join the march. If they did, no animals of this kind would be left. Some remain at home and continue to raise young. Family after family is born. For them, life goes on until they die from hunger, disease or become food for another animal. Or they live until there is another march to the sea from which they will never return.

Many people have suggested reasons for the journey to the sea. Perhaps the lemmings are seeking greater supplies of food. Perhaps they are sick with a disease that stimulates them so that they march on

Lemmings

and on and on. Dr. Edward S. Deevey, of Yale University, thinks the latter is true. He believes that their endocrine glands produce hormones which make them use their energy rapidly. Some may die from shock, or from a liver disease, or high blood pressure, and some may even scare each other to death before they reach the sea. Perhaps those which reach the sea think that it is another small body of water across which they can swim. But why do the lemmings always travel on and on until they reach the sea? No one can answer this question.

What leads the lemmings to the sea? What directs their built-in compass? Here are more questions without answers. No lemming that makes a journey to the sea has ever made it before, for none comes back to its home from this kind of march.

MICE, DOGS, AND CATS

Interesting experiments are being performed with some small mammals that show an ability to find their own homes. Some wild mice of the white-footed variety are known not to roam farther than several hundred feet from their homes. Some of these animals were tagged and taken much farther away. Many were able to return from much longer distances, five from as far as a mile away, while one managed to get home from a distance of one and a half miles, even though it had never been so far away before. Certainly, they used some methods other than landmarks, but no one knows exactly what they used for a compass.

Dogs and cats are well known for their journeys home over unfamiliar ground. From time to time, articles in the newspaper tell of animals that return to their owners from distances of hundreds of miles even though they have never made the journey before. They walk for days, swim across rivers, and reach home by using some method that is not understood. Unfortunately, many lost dogs and cats are unable to do this, while others who have been moved to a distant home on purpose, manage to reach their original masters.

There is still much mystery about the way mammals find their way both to their permanent and to their seasonal homes. And what provides the urge for them to move from place to place? What sets the clock?

*Woodchuck,
often called a groundhog.*

8. Animal Clocks and Space Travel

CLOCKS OF HIBERNATORS

By studying the built-in clocks of some animals, men may be able to help themselves on their trips into space. These animals are the hibernators, those who spend the winter in a strange state where their body systems almost cease to function. Perhaps man can learn to hibernate and use this state on his spaceships.

Imagine a woodchuck, or groundhog, getting ready for winter. He has been eating well all summer.

Lately, he stuffed himself until he became four times as fat as normal. In addition to the regular fat which is present, there is some dark fat which has accumulated around the blood vessels in certain parts of his body. This kind of fat is known to decrease at a slower rate than normal fat.

Soon temperatures will fall and food will grow scarce. Some scientists believe that the extra deposits of fat trigger hibernation rather than lack of food or falling temperature. In a certain part of the woodchuck's brain—the hypothalamus—there are nerve cells which control many vital functions including the condition of being awake or asleep. When the temperature remains at 50 degrees for several days, this part of his brain tells him to enter his deep, deep winter sleep.

The woodchuck has been growing drowsier and drowsier, until he can no longer stay awake. He waddles along the tunnels of his underground burrow and curls up with his head tucked beneath his tail. His body temperature grows lower and lower, his heartbeat slows down, and a mere trickle of air enters his lungs. The woodchuck's pulse grows weaker and his temperature drops to 45 degrees. He is ready for weeks of deep, deep sleep during which all his body processes will be slowed down. During normal sleep, only some processes are slower and body temperature is normal. Hibernation is very different from this.

During hibernation, a woodchuck does not eat.

The white cells from his circulatory system have already moved into his stomach, where they absorbed and destroyed the bacteria which would decay any food that remained there during hibernation. Then these white cells returned to the blood stream. Throughout the winter while he sleeps, a woodchuck does not digest any food in his stomach. He uses the stored fat for the small amount of energy which he needs to carry on his life processes. He would not even hear you if you called, nor would he notice if you touched him.

What sets the clock that wakes a hibernating animal from his winter condition? Dr. Charles P. Lyman of the Museum of Comparative Anatomy of Harvard University believes that the accumulation of waste material might play a part in waking the woodchuck in the spring even thought he does wake from time to time during the winter in order to rid himself of waste matter. In the spring he uncurls a bit and flickers his eyelids. He moves his paws as though he is having a dream. His body temperature rises and his heart beats very fast. Several hours go by while he gradually awakens. He gets to his feet and is ready to go outdoors. His clock has fully awakened him from his winter hibernation, and his long sleep is over. Superstitious people believe he will go back to hibernate longer if he sees his shadow on Groundhog Day. Then, according to them, winter will continue. If he has just come out to get rid of waste matter on this day, and is not fully awake, he will go back to sleep. Naturally, whether he comes out or not, has no influence on the local weather.

Suppose man can learn to imitate the winter-sleeping animals and be induced into a state of hibernation on a space ship. For a long trip the problem of carrying food is a big one. A hibernating man would not need as much food. And if the trip is long, boredom is a big problem. In a state of hibernation, time would pass unnoticed.

Much more must be learned about the animal clocks of hibernators and about the state of hibernation before man can hope to induce such a state in himself. Scientists are inducing hibernation all year round in animals that normally spend the winters this way. Dr. Lyman keeps animals in small wire cages in the Harvard Medical School where the temperature is about 40 degrees all the time. Some of the animals hibernate even in the summertime. But they do not stay this way indefinitely.

Golden hamsters are among the animals which are being watched in the laboratory. When their clocks are set for hibernation, their heartbeats slow down from 400 beats a minute to 4 beats per minute. They breathe only once every two minutes and they use only a small amount of oxygen. But after several weeks, they tense their muscles and they gradually awaken.

In an effort to find out what sets the clocks of hibernating animals, scientists at the University of Toronto

Hamsters are useful laboratory animals.

in Canada kept a squirrel in a room where the temperature was about 35 degrees, and where the light was kept on for twelve hours each day. The squirrel hibernated from October through May, even though the temperature did not change. From this, it seems that cold alone does not set the clock.

Certainly, there is much to learn about hibernation. Scientists are studying this strange condition in laboratories in many parts of the world. Perhaps someday they will learn how to apply it to human beings.

HUMAN CLOCKS

Even though people do not have internal clocks which are set for hibernation, they do show a sense of time. This is more true with some people than with others. Do you know someone who can plan to awaken at a certain time in the morning and do so? Such people are seldom more than fifteen minutes off schedule. Scientists who have studied this ability at Princeton University believe that every cell in the brain contains a sort of internal clock which marks time. But they do not know how some people can set their biological clocks.

Each person uses a day-night cycle of rest and wakefulness and has a regular body pattern that repeats itself day after day. The temperature of the body drops a fraction of a degree at bedtime, and it may drop a degree or more during the night. When a person arises in the morning, his temperature climbs back to its normal level. In some individuals, body temperature climbs rapidly and they are ready to work efficiently soon after they get up in the morning. In other cases, body temperature rises slowly. These people are more efficient later in the day. People can be classified as day people or night people according to the way their internal clocks run. Day people are happy at breakfast time and feel alert first thing in the morning. Night people are often irritable soon after they get up. You can experiment to see which class you and your friends belong to by following directions in the next chapter. In this way, you can see if your guesses as to which group they belong are right. Even children can be grouped as day and night people, for internal clocks seem to set themselves at the age of two years.

Even before men thought much about the artificial days and nights which will be used in space travel, men experimented with changing the twenty-four-hour cycle to which the human body is adjusted. Dr. Nathaniel Kleitman of the University of Chicago and one of his students experimented about twenty years ago in a large chamber in Mammoth Cave, Kentucky, to see how man can adapt himself to an artificial day-night cycle. They lived on a twenty-eight-hour schedule instead of the normal twenty-four-hour one. Dr. Kleitman at the age of forty-three had a more difficult time adjusting to the schedule than did his student. Within a week, the student's body temperature pattern had shifted to the new schedule. Dr. Kleitman's experiments did show that man is able to reset his internal clock, even though it is more difficult for some individuals than for others.

People must reset their own regular day-night rhythms when they take long plane journeys from east to west or in the opposite direction. Suppose you have

As school opens in the morning in Florida children in Alaskan schools are eating lunch.

116

lived in New York where you normally rise at seven in the morning. A plane carries you to California in a few hours where you go to bed and arise at California time which is three hours later than New York time. You may find yourself waking at four o'clock in the morning for several days until your body resets its clock.

When men travel into space, there will be no regular periods of dark and light, for day on earth is caused by the turning of the planet on which we live. Outer space is dark hour after hour, with no sunrise and no sunset. The stars are always shining in the sky. Here man can make his own periods of day and night. But how will his internal clock adjust to artificial periods?

A day and night cycle of waking and sleeping are part of efficient living. Dr. Hubertus Strughold, who is one of the world's leading authorities on space medicine, believes that this cycle must be regarded as a biological law. If it is ignored for too long a period of time, it can cause a nervous breakdown; but experiments seem to show that the cycle can be modified.

Men have experimented with day-night cycles of different lengths in their earth-bound space ships. For instance, when Airman Donald G. Farrell completed a seven-day simulated flight to the moon and back in a space cabin at Randolph Air Force Base in Texas, he lived on an artificial day-night cycle. His day was fourteen hours long, consisting of four and a half hours for sleep, four hours for work periods, and half-hour periods for personal hygiene and eating.

Perhaps space men will set their internal clocks on new schedules before traveling into space, for there they can make their own day and night at the intervals which suit them best.

MOTION AND TIME

No one questions the fact that there will not be days and nights in space such as there are on earth; but not long ago, scientists disagreed about another problem concerning time and space. There is a theory that when space ships start approaching the speed of light, which is 186,000 miles per second, time will slow down. This theory was derived from Einstein's theory of relativity.

According to Einstein, nothing can travel faster than the speed of light, but scientists are trying to perfect a method of space propulsion which may someday enable men to approach such speeds. By shooting incredibly concentrated beams of light, or photons, from the tail of a rocket ship, men may travel to Mars in thirty-five hours, to Jupiter in four days, and to Saturn in six days. They may even travel beyond the sun's planets to other solar systems where planets are spinning around other stars. All this may be very far in the future, but it does seem probable to many serious scientists. When this happens, what will happen to man's built-in time clock if it is true that time

118

slows down when one travels at a speed near that of light?

Suppose a space traveler has a twin which he leaves here on earth. In a space ship that travels about two-thirds the speed of light, he visits the area of the star Sirius. The twin who remains at home waits for eighteen years. During that time his biological processes make his body eighteen years older. But the twin who is traveling in space does not age that much. For him time passes more slowly even though it does not

seem that way. His wrist watch ticks more slowly, his heart beats more slowly, his body tissues wear out more slowly, and he ages more slowly. During the trip to Sirius and back, he ages about five or six years less than his earth-bound brother.

Although some people have compared an ultra-fast space ship to a fountain of youth, travelers would not regain their youth. Their life span would be increased, though, for they would not age as fast.

Men, women, and children may go to the distant stars and return young, even though hundreds of years have passed on earth. They may even travel to a distant galaxy in one generation while the earth passes through a billion years. What would the crew come home to? It has been estimated that a trip around the universe aboard a photon ship would take about forty-two years. During this time, the earth would have passed through several billion years and might even have crumbled into cosmic dust. Space travelers dream of these days, but no one need worry about such a problem right now. There are many other problems to be solved before man can take even a short trip in a photon-propelled space ship. Such a ship has not even been built.

Perhaps you find it hard to believe that time will really slow down when such high velocities are reached. Even scientists questioned this; but now there is some experimental evidence that this will happen. Scientists have tested this theory by measuring the life of small particles of matter known as mesons. These particles which are even smaller than atoms, are created high in the atmosphere by cosmic rays. They shoot toward the earth at a speed approaching that of light. Mesons can be used to test the time-space theory because mesons decay, or change into other particles. Their normal rate of decay has been measured, and the rate at which fast-traveling mesons decay has been measured. It was found that fast-moving mesons decayed more slowly than stationary ones. Their clocks are slowed in flight, and they live about fifteen times longer.

Scientists are planning another experiment that will check another Einstein theory but may also show that time is influenced by motion. An atomic clock is being built at the Hughes Aircraft Company in California which is so accurate that it will neither gain nor lose one second in a thousand years. When the clock is finished, scientists plan to place it in a satellite to orbit the earth at 18,000 miles per hour. The atomic clock will send its time-readings by radio to men on the earth. These readings can be compared with the time on another atomic clock on the ground. The difference in time will be very small, for the satellite will travel much slower than the speed of light. But with such accurate clocks even unbelievably small changes can be measured. On the satellites that travel closest to the earth, the difference will be only .01 second per year.

Dr. Harold Lyons, inventor of the world's first atomic clock, believes that when atomic clocks become more and more accurate, it may be possible to measure the difference in time-readings in fast-flying planes. These differences would, of course, be extremely minute, and no change would be noticeable in the rate of aging between people traveling on fast planes and those who remain on earth any more than is noticed today. Changes in internal time clocks would have to last for long periods of time on space trips of the distant future before any difference would be noticed on returning to earth. Even then, a person on a space ship could not sense the slackening of time. Only when he reached home and compared the aging of his own body with that of someone who had remained on earth would he be able to notice any difference.

Long before man learns to travel near the speed of light, he may learn how to set his internal clock and hibernate the way some animals do. This, too, may be years away, but scientists are working toward the day when man can influence his own internal clock.

9. A Puzzle for Tomorrow

There are many pieces to the puzzle of animal clocks and compasses. In fact, there are *many different* puzzles since there are many different animals that are influenced by regular rhythms and have special abilities that enable them to find their ways. In spite of the experiments of many scientists, there are still a great number of pieces missing in the puzzles. But bit by bit, information is being added to what is already known, and new ideas are taking the place of older ones.

COMPASS PUZZLES

No one knows how many different kinds of animals navigate by sun or star compasses the way certain birds and fish seem to be able to navigate. Perhaps there are many others which navigate in this way.

Scientists are still experimenting in this field. For instance, there are large green turtles that feed at sea hundreds of miles from the beaches where they lay their eggs each year. Like the salmon and the eels, these reptiles return to the place of their birth to lay their eggs. No one knows exactly how they find their way, but Dr. Archie Carr, of the University of Florida, is experimenting to find out how. He will fasten orange balloons filled with helium to a large number of turtles which are going from the sea to the shore where they will lay their eggs. The helium will keep the balloons high above the water, and the orange color will make each one easy to see. In this way, he can track turtles during the day from a shrimp boat on which he will follow their path. At night Dr. Carr will listen to small transistor radios with 6-inch antennas that he will have fastened to the migrating turtles. He expects to find that the turtles travel underwater in a straight line toward the beach, coming to the sur-

*Large green
sea turtle*

face only to breathe and get their bearings from the sun and stars. What he learns may add one more small piece to the puzzle of animal compasses.

Certainly, no one teaches the turtles where to go to lay their eggs. It seems that they must be born knowing where to go. Salmon, too, seem to be born with built-in compasses that enable them to go to sea and return to the very place where they were hatched to produce the next generation. But an experiment with young fish adds to the puzzle. Eggs of salmon were taken from one stream and placed in another to see if the hatched fish learned to know their home stream or whether they were born knowing it. The Columbia River in Canada and the Willamette River in Oregon both empty into the Lower Columbia River. The salmon of the Columbia River run in the autumn, while those in the Willamette run in the spring. Some eggs were taken from the place where they were laid in the Willamette River and were hatched in the Columbia River. The young fish were confined until they were between seven and eighteen months old. Before they were set free, the fish were marked so that they could be identified when they returned from the sea. Would they return to the Willamette River where they were born or to the Columbia River where they were hatched?

Four to five years after the marked salmon were released, they returned to spawn in the Columbia River where they were hatched. Here they were

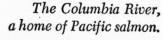

The Columbia River, a home of Pacific salmon.

trapped and identified. They came up the river in the spring, at the same time of the year when their parents had returned to the other river to spawn. The real inhabitants of the Columbia River came in the fall. From this, it seems that a part of the built-in compass was not inherited, for the salmon learned to recognize the river in which they were hatched. On the other hand, their built-in clocks brought them back at the same season as the one in which their parents returned.

Men are just beginning to learn how many kinds of animals find their way. Additional experiments may someday solve the many riddles that exist concerning animal compasses. In the meantime, men will continue to marvel at the way animals can navigate. Often they manage better than man with all his expensive and complex instruments.

CLOCK PUZZLES

Is the twenty-four-hour rhythm which so many animals exhibit an inherited one, or is it influenced by something outside the animal? The traveling bees described earlier in this book seemed to have internally-controlled clocks. But were all outside conditions controlled?

Here is another experiment which might lead one to believe that animals can measure time without outside influence. Vinegar flies, the little flies that gather around over-ripe fruit in great numbers, are known to begin their adult lives at dawn when the night's humidity is high and they can most easily spread their

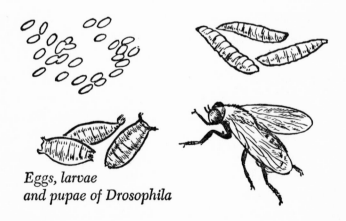

Eggs, larvae and pupae of Drosophila

wings. If the young flies are kept in complete darkness while they are developing, they will emerge at various times. If they are taken from a room where they were exposed to normal periods of day and night, and are put in the dark the flies can continue to keep accurate count of the day and night and emerge at the proper time a whole week later.

Suppose the flies are exposed to a single flash of light for as short a time as one minute. This light is enough to set their clocks. They will emerge from their pupal cases at the same time of the day as the time the light flash was given. Such a light flash could not have taught them anything about a twenty-four-hour cycle of day and night, but it set their built-in clocks on such a cycle with the light flash acting as dawn. Their internal clocks measure off the twenty-four-hour periods even though they have never experienced such a period of night and day.

Are there some other forces which act on living things in a subtle, still unknown way? Might these forces give vinegar flies and other living things the ability to measure off periods which correspond to the natural night and day? Are the internal clocks really controlled entirely inside the animal, or are they influenced by some force in the environment, perhaps from outer space? This problem is an exciting challenge to the scientists who study it.

Dr. Frank A. Brown of Northwestern University in Evanston, Illinois, has spent many year analyzing and sorting information about living clocks, and he has performed many experiments in timing them. Some of the results are especially interesting.

Here are some of the things which Dr. Brown has learned about whether or not the built-in clocks of animals are entirely controlled inside of the animals. Using a batch of oysters which were sent from New Haven, Connecticut, Dr. Brown and his fellow scien-

Oyster

tists reset the time at which they opened their shells the widest. In New Haven Harbor, the oysters opened their shells the widest at the time of high tide there. When shipped to Evanston, Illinois, they continued to open their shells widest on New Haven time. But after two weeks they forgot their home time and opened their shells widest when there was the greatest amount of gravitational attraction by the moon in Evanston. Here, daily rhythms seem to be influenced by an outside force—the attraction between moon and earth which is greatest at high tide.

STRANGE WEATHERMEN

There are twenty-four-hour rhythms that depend on universal time. One is a difference in the electrical charge between the earth and the sky. This fluctuates daily within a twenty-four-hour cycle. Could animals have some kind of apparatus for sensing such a change and set their clocks with it?

To learn more about whether or not some rhythm of universal time might be influencing animal clocks, Dr. Brown first studied metabolism, the biological process of using food for energy and growth. This process is common to all living things. Every plant and animal must use energy in order to live, and the rate at which it uses energy can be measured by the rate at which the living thing uses oxygen. This rate varies with a twenty-four-hour rhythm.

Potatoes were chosen to act as guinea pigs in many of the experiments. You may not think of potatoes as having metabolism, but they do. They use energy to sprout and grow into new plants. You might not think of potatoes as having rhythm, or daily cycles, either. For these reasons, potatoes seemed like good material for experiments. Another reason for choosing them was the large amounts of food which they store, making it unnecessary to feed them. They can be kept alive in dark and constant conditions without being supplied with any type of nourishment.

Potatoes make strange weathermen; but in a sense, they are just that. To understand why, you must first know that there are daily rhythms in the amount of atmosphere which presses on the earth. This is measured by a barometer, and is known as barometric pressure. On the average, barometric pressure rises during the early morning hours until about ten o'clock in the morning, then it falls to the low point for the day in the middle or late afternoon. This rhythm repeats itself day after day. Some days the barometric pressure is greater than others, depending on the weather.

Dr. Brown found that potatoes show a daily cycle in their rate of metabolism. The greatest rate occurs at six in the afternoon, and the lowest rate at midnight. And potatoes, too, show variations in rate from day to day. Strange as it may seem, the potatoes' rate of metabolism and the speed at which the barometric pressure falls and rises are related. The potatoes are informed of the barometric pressure, even though they are in hermetically sealed containers, for their rate of metabolism on any given day is related to how fast the barometric pressure was changing on the afternoon of the day before.

Anyone can tell the barometric pressure and the related weather of yesterday. But the potatoes do more than that. The potatoes know what the change will be the day after tomorrow. It was evident in their rate of metabolism that they could anticipate the weather changes two days in advance!

Dr. Brown experimented with other living things, too, to see if they had metabolism rates that were related to changes in barometric pressure. He used oysters, seaweeds, salamanders, crabs, and carrots. All of these showed the same kind of variation and pre-

Spotted salamander

dicted barometric pressure changes two days in advance. All of these are strange weathermen. How, Dr. Brown jokingly asks, might a human weatherman fare if he took the place of a potato and were kept in constant conditions for weeks, or months? Could he give a two-day weather prediction? Or could he even tell the weather today?

In Dr. Brown's experiments, the living things showed relationships to the outside world other than those with barometric pressure. The change in metabolism rate of potatoes and the outside temperature were related, and there was evidence of relationship with the daily rhythm of energy from outer space known as high-energy background radiation. This kind of energy penetrates all ordinary buildings and containers. Although it follows a regular pattern, or cycle, within twenty-four hours, it varies from day to day in a way that cannot be predicted. In some way, the potatoes in the sealed containers had knowledge of this variation. The greater the change in the amount of radiation yesterday, the greater the change in metabolism today.

This is just some of the information which Dr. Frank Brown has gathered from his many experiments on the rhythmic nature of animals and plants. From his work, it seems evident that the built-in clocks of animals are receiving information from outside forces. Certainly, each animal is born with a blueprint for its life, but that blueprint is modified by outside forces. This is true of the internal clocks, for no animal could be born with a complete knowledge of daily changes in barometric pressure, temperature, background radiation, and other cycles.

How do outside forces affect animal clocks? This is a great challenge to the biologists of tomorrow. Perhaps the answer to this question will lead to new knowledge about migration and animal navigation.

As man learns more about animal clocks and compasses, he adds to the knowledge of his own behavior, for there are great potentials for the use of such information in biology and medicine. The fact that living things are responding to factors that were once considered completely disconnected from them may be a stepping stone to much important knowledge.

Certainly, there is a great amount of work to be done before all the riddles of animal clocks and compasses are solved; but someday, all of the pieces of the puzzle will fit together. In the meantime, animals around the world are guiding themselves to the right place at the right time with their mysterious clocks and compasses.

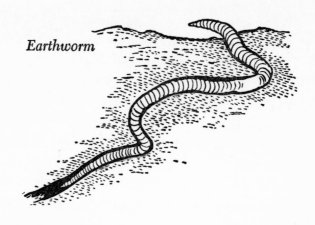

Earthworm

10. Science Projects

Perhaps you would like to learn more about animal clocks and compasses by doing some observing of your own. Here are some experiments which you can do at home with such animals as earthworms, frogs, and vinegar flies. You can begin preparations for the hobby of bird banding. And you can even experiment with human clocks on yourself and your friends.

Earthworms and Artificial Winters

SUGGESTIONS FOR EXPERIMENTS

Put individual earthworms in about five separate jars of slightly moistened soil. Place each jar at a different temperature for several hours. Keep one of the jars in the refrigerator. Then remove the worms from the jars and lay them on newspaper with the flattened part down. Watch for regular pulses which are caused by the blood moving toward the head. How is the speed of this circulation changed by the temperature of the surroundings? What effect does cold have on the rate of the earthworm's body activities? Does it influence their metabolic clocks?

HOW TO CARE FOR EARTHWORMS

Earthworms can be kept alive for long periods of time in a wooden box that has been filled as follows: Place an inch of leaf mold in the bottom of the box, then add an inch of loamy soil, an inch of leaves, and an inch of soil. Continue this until the box is about two-thirds filled. Cover the box with moist corrugated cardboard and place it in a cool, dark place. Sprinkle water over the cardboard every few days, but do not use so much that the cardboard gets soggy. You do not need to feed the earthworms. They will feed on the leaves in the box.

Frogs and Artificial Winters

SUGGESTIONS FOR EXPERIMENTS

In nature, leopard frogs become quiet in September. The following month, they crawl under stones in shallow brooks, or they burrow under the soft mud at the bottom of ponds where they will spend the winter. Does temperature set the clock for this hibernation? Does light play a part?

1. You can make artificial winters and artificial days and nights for frogs in your own home. A frog's eating habits and activity rate vary with temperature changes. By placing frogs in a cold place, such as a cold porch, outdoors, in a basement, or in a refrigerator, you can observe these changes. You can even put the frogs in a tub of ice cubes for a time. This will not injure them. Frogs that were frozen into ice in experiments survived as long as the deep blood vessels and the heart were not frozen. In nature, leopard frogs can survive freezing in the bottoms of shallow ponds.

Record the temperature of each place where frogs are kept and the length of time they remain at that

Leopard frog

temperature. Note how long it takes them to become active after being in a cold place. Observe the breathing rate as indicated by the up and down movement of the lower jaw. Does the degree of cold make a difference? Does the length of time in each place make a difference? Vary the length of time and vary the temperature, making notes of each. Can you draw a graph to represent your results?

2. Does light have an effect on frog activity? It has been found that toads which are kept at a temperature of 60 degrees Fahrenheit are sluggish and refuse to eat all through the winter. This is not very cold. Might day length play a part? Experiment with various day lengths by covering your frogs' living quarters with dark cloth and by exposing them to long periods of artificial light. Try flashes of light to interrupt the long periods of dark. What happens when frogs are kept warm and in constant light?

3. Frogs swim upward and downward according to the temperature. Put your frogs in an aquarium full of water. There is a certain temperature at which they will go to the bottom and crawl under the rocks with their heads pointed down and their hind legs sprawled outward. You can find this by cooling the water with ice and watching an aquarium thermometer.

HOW TO OBTAIN FROGS

If it is spring or summer, you may be able to catch a frog in a local pond. If not, try a biological supply house. You can find one in your telephone book or from your biology teacher. Rana pipiens is a good leopard frog to order. It is about 2 to 4 inches long, and has dark spots surrounded by white, on green or olive-colored skin. This is a common frog, so it may be less expensive.

Sometimes frogs may be obtained without charge from medical laboratories and hospitals where they have been used for tests. Call first, and take a container with you if the technicians are willing to supply frogs for your experiments.

HOW TO CARE FOR FROGS

Suitable quarters for frogs can be made in an aquarium or large glass tank in which semiaquatic conditions have been created. Cover the bottom with gravel, and arrange a landing place for the frogs at one end. Pieces of wood or stones can be placed across the aquarium to prevent the landing place from sliding. The water part should be about 2 inches deep.

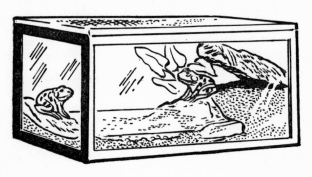

A curved piece of bark makes a pleasant hiding place for frogs. Be sure to secure a wire mesh top over the terrarium so that the frogs cannot jump out.

Frogs should be fed one good meal per week, except in very warm weather when they require two meals. When the frogs are kept at a low temperature, they require no food at all. Raw liver may be used as food all through the winter, and a supply can be kept in a freezer. Dangle it from a string in front of the frog's mouth. Flies and other insects should be used when they are available. Small earthworms and mealworms may be used, too. Feed a frog as much as it will consume at one time, and remove any uneaten food after a few hours so that it does not decay in the terrarium. A drop or two of cod liver oil placed on the food at each meal helps to keep frogs in good condition.

Drosophila and Animal Clocks

SUGGESTIONS FOR EXPERIMENTS

1. Begin by raising a few generations of vinegar flies. These are commonly called fruit flies and have the scientific name of Drosophila melanogaster. Directions are given below. Record the time it takes for each stage to develop and the temperature at which the flies are kept. Records can be pasted to individual bottles or the bottles can be numbered and records kept in a notebook.

2. When you are familiar with the procedure of raising flies, vary the temperature of different bottles. Put some in the refrigerator, others in a warm place. Note how this changes the rate of development.

3. Try different day lengths, covering some before natural sunset, covering others the entire time. You can increase the periods of darkness by wrapping the bottles in dark cloth. And you can increase the periods

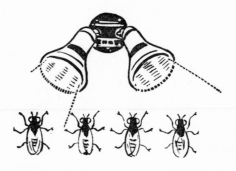

of light by using electric lights. This will make an artificially long day.

4. Interrupt your artificial night with flashes of light. Does this change the clocks of vinegar flies?

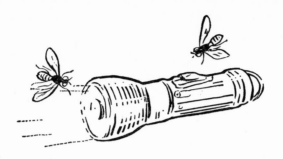

HOW TO OBTAIN DROSOPHILA

In the summertime, a piece of over-ripe fruit in an open jar will attract enough flies for experiments; but at other seasons, a biological supply house or college laboratory can be a good source.

HOW TO BREED DROSOPHILA

You may be able to raise enough flies for some simple experiments in a cotton-stoppered jar which contains a piece of ripe banana. Flies lay eggs on the banana and the larvae and pupae may be transferred to other jars with pieces of ripe banana in them.

If you wish to do serious projects, superior culture methods should replace the banana culture. Here is a formula that is used in many science laboratories:

10 grams agar agar (drug store)	yeast cake
50 grams corn meal	Moldex from biological supply house if possible
35 c.c. corn syrup	
35 c.c. dark molasses	
500 c.c. water	

Add the agar agar to the water in a saucepan and bring the mixture to a boil. Add Moldex, if available, to prevent molding. Add the corn meal slowly, while stirring constantly. When this is well mixed, add the syrup and molasses and allow the mixture to boil for ten minutes. Do not overcook, for this will cause the mixture to harden in the pan.

Pour the mixture into quart milk bottles so that there is about 2 inches on the bottom of each bottle. Place a strip of paper toweling into the warm mixture so that it stands along the side and provides a place for the flies to crawl.

Allow the mixture to harden. When you are ready to use a bottle, dissolve a small portion of a fresh yeast cake in water and apply one drop with a medicine dropper. Keep the remaining yeast in the refrigerator. Do not add the yeast to the bottles which will not be used immediately. Use cotton plugs for the tops of bottles after flies have been added.

LIFE HISTORY OF DROSOPHILA

Drosophila, like other flies, develop in four stages. The eggs usually hatch into larvae about 24 hours after they have been laid. The larvae molt two times. If the room temperature is warm, this may occur twenty-four hours and forty-eight hours after hatching from the egg. In cooler temperatures, the development is slower. Larvae become pupae about ninety-six hours after hatching if the temperature is about 77 degrees Fahrenheit. Several hours after the larvae pupate, they stop feeding and crawl onto the side of the culture bottle. The fully formed pupa is brown, oval, and smooth. After about ninety-six hours, at 77 degrees Fahrenheit, the adult emerges through a flap at the front end of the pupal case. If the flies are kept at a lower temperature, development takes longer. Total development, from egg to adult, may be about twelve days at room temperature. In any case, wings do not unfold for about thirty minutes after the adult has emerged. Adult flies can be anesthetized with ether and examined under a magnifying glass.

Bird Banding

Bird banding is an exciting hobby which can be enjoyed for a lifetime, but it requires some serious preparation. To obtain a license as a bird bander, one must meet certain requirements. Even though one of these is being eighteen years of age, younger people may begin preparations before that time. Imagine the thrill of being notified that a bird which you banded was recovered thousands of miles away.

Atlantic flyway is the path of many land birds and water-fowl from Greenland, New England, and eastern Canada.

Many volunteers who enjoy this sport find it so fascinating that they continue to band birds with great enthusiasm over a period of years. One man who began in 1913 retired in 1958 at the age of eighty-seven. He had banded about 50,000 birds of 130 different species.

1. There are a number of ways to begin preparations. First, you might write to the Bird Banding Office, Patuxent Wildlife Research Center, Laurel, Maryland, to get the details of the requirements.

Mississippi flyway is the most heavily traveled. Well-watered forests and fields stretch out for thousands of miles and no mountains interfere.

You might also write to your state capital for information about state projects. Address your letter to State Game Department, your state capital.

2. All bird banders must be able to identify a large number of birds, for it is a cardinal rule of the program never to band a bird without being certain of its identity. Many persons who report finding bands have little knowledge of what kind of bird they have recovered, so positive identification depends upon the person who applies the band.

Since it takes much time and effort to be able to identify a wide variety of birds, here is a good place

Central flyway is a highway for many birds from the Rocky Mountains and Great Plains.

for a future bird bander to begin. You may wish to keep a record of the kinds of birds that you can recognize and make a report in your book each time that you see one of the more unusual birds. Enter information about the place and the date, and compare this information with the migration habits of the birds. You may wish to make a map of migration routes, too.

3. While you are learning to recognize birds, you can also become better acquainted with the banding program. *Bird Banding* is a technical journal which is published by the Northeastern Bird Banding Association, 47 Scotland Road, Reading, Massachusetts.

Pacific flyway serves Alaska, western Canada, and the Pacific States.

4. You can watch for dead birds with the hope of finding one with a band. Thousands of people find banded birds each year. Some game birds are shot down by hunters who send in the bands and receive information about the past of their kills. They remove the aluminum bands with screw drivers, send them with letters to the U.S. Fish and Wildlife Service, Patuxent Research Refuge, Laurel, Maryland, where Civil Service workers check the files for information about the birds who carried these numbered bands. Letters from the Bird Banding Office go back to the hunters telling them when and where the birds were banded. The information which the hunters sent, helps the Bird Banding Office, and the information which the hunters receive makes their kill more interesting.

Many banded birds are washed ashore on the beaches and are found by surf fishermen and others who walk along the edge of the surf. You may find dead birds along the roadside where they have been killed by automobiles or fallen after flying into telephone wires or other obstacles. Birds are sometimes found dead at feeding stations.

5. After receiving your license, you can set traps and recover healthy birds. You must tend your nets and traps frequently, for a catch must be removed before half an hour has passed. You will keep complete records on forms which will be supplied by the Fish and Wildlife Service, and you will keep a supply of

numbered bands of various sizes which will be sent to you without charge along with the forms. Bands for small birds must be extremely small. Those for chickadees and warblers are only about as large as the head of a kitchen match. Applying such bands is not easy, for they must be loose enough to slide up and down the leg, but not so loose that they will work off over the foot. Learning to apply bands is another part of the preparation of a bird bander.

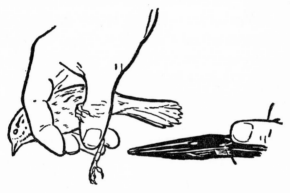

6. If you live near a zoo, a museum of natural science, or a university, you may be able to talk with people who are authorities on birds and who can direct you to local people who are licensed bird banders. Perhaps you can attend their local meetings.

Human Clocks

1. Can you awaken at a certain time without the help of an alarm clock? Try this for several nights.

Before going to sleep, think about the time you want to arise and do not set the alarm. Choose a time that is earlier than the one when you must get up, so someone in your family can awaken you in case your natural alarm does not work.

Keep a record of the number of times you can awaken yourself near the planned time. See if you can improve with practice.

2. Try to estimate the passing of time while you are awake. Some people have internal clocks which are synchronized with their watches. They can guess what time it is within about ten minutes. Experiment with your friends' mental clocks, keeping a record of how far from the correct time their guesses are. And how do they rate in guessing the correct passing of time. Are some more accurate than others? Are those people the ones who are able to set their built-in alarm clocks by just thinking about when they want to awaken?

3. You can do an interesting experiment with day and night people if some of your friends are willing to cooperate. Provide each one with a form on which to record his temperature on arising, his temperature three hours after arising, and his temperature on retiring. See if the "morning people" have faster rises in temperature. Identify each person as a morning or evening person before beginning this experiment. The people who live with each friend can help you to do this.

4. Perhaps you will want to find out if day people are more accurate in estimating the passing of time than night people. Can they use internal alarm clocks more easily than night people?

Scientists for Tomorrow

These are just a few projects in which you can begin your work in the world of animal clocks and compasses. Even if you never become a scientist, you may find a great deal of pleasure in searching for more information about animals. With so many unsolved problems remaining, it is obvious that there is still much work to be done. Perhaps you will find your first projects so exciting that you may eventually choose a career in which you can join the men and women who are searching for the answers to the wonders of animal clocks and compasses.

Male Drosophila

 **Bibliography**

Blond, Georges, *The Great Migrations*, New York, The Macmillan Company, 1956

Carthy, J. D., *Animal Navigation*, New York, Charles Scribner's Sons, 1956

Fisher, James, *Watching Birds*, Middlesex, England, A Pelican Book, 1951

Griffin, Donald R., *Echoes of Bats and Men*, Garden City, New York, Doubleday and Company, Inc., 1959

Griffin, Donald R. *Listening in the Dark*, New Haven, Connecticut, Yale University Press, 1958

Migration of Birds, Washington, D.C., Fish and Wildlife Service, U.S. Department of the Interior, Circular 16

Milne, Lorus and Margery, *Paths across the Earth*, New York, Harper and Brothers, 1958

Peterson, Roger Tory, *The Bird Watcher's Anthology*, New York, Harcourt, Brace and Company, 1957

Williams, C. B., *Insect Migration*, New York, The Macmillan Company, 1959

Index

About the Author and Artist

MARGARET O. HYDE has long been interested in science. Returning to Columbia University, where she received her master's degree, she became science consultant at the Lincoln School of Teachers College, Columbia. She has also been head of the Science Department at the Shipley School, Bryn Mawr, Pennsylvania, and a lecturer in elementary education at Temple University.

Her other junior books, *Atoms Today and Tomorrow*, *Driving Today and Tomorrow*, *Flight Today and Tomorrow*, *Medicine in Action*, *Exploring Earth and Space*, *From Submarines to Satellites*, *Off into Space!*, *Plants Today and Tomorrow*, and *Where Speed Is King* (with her husband Edwin Hyde), have been widely applauded. She and her husband live in Glenside, Pennsylvania, and have two children.

P. A. HUTCHISON has illustrated many books, including *Call of the White Fox* and *Alaska, the Forty-Ninth State* by Willis Lindquist, *Man and His Tools* by William A. Burns, *Cave of Riches* by Alan Honour, and *Plants Today and Tomorrow* by Margaret O. Hyde. Miss Hutchison was born in Montana, studied at the University of Washington, and was a member of the Illustration Corps at the American Museum of Natural History.